ALSO BY FRANK McCLAIN

IT Questions & Answers For IT Job Interviews, Volume 2

IPv4 and IPv6 Addressing, NAT, Layer 2 Switching Concepts,
Layer 3 Routing Concepts

IT Questions & Answers For IT Job Interviews, Volume 3

BGP Routing, EIGRP Routing, OSPF Routing

IT Questions & Answers For IT Job Interviews, Volume 4

Data Center and Virtualization, F5 Networks Load Balancer,
Riverbed WAN Optimization

IT Questions & Answers For IT Job Interviews, Volume 5

Access Lists and Prefix Lists, Tunnels and VPNs, Cisco ASA Firewall

IT Questions & Answers For IT Job Interviews, Volume 6

Service Provider Networks, Quality of Service (QoS),
Troubleshooting Router and Switch Interfaces

The Ultimate Job Hunting Guidebook

The multi-award-winning *The Ultimate Job Hunting Guidebook*
won the **Foreword Reviews'** prestigious *Foreword INDIES
Book of the Year Award*.

The Ultimate Job Hunting Guidebook for Military Veterans

YOU'RE HIRED!

Winner of the **Independent Book Publishers Association**
Benjamin Franklin Digital Award. Success secrets to phone and in-
person job interviews for job seekers and career changers.

IT Questions & Answers
For IT Job Interviews

Volume 1

General IT Knowledge / Transmission Lines and Cabling
Voice over IP (VoIP) / Video and Telepresence over IP
Wireless (Wi-Fi)

Frank McClain

Warning and Disclaimer

This book is designed to provide information about network responsibilities, issues, programs, applications, and equipment related to this subject. Every effort has been made to make this book as complete and accurate as possible, but no warranty or fitness is implied by the author or publisher.

The information in this book is provided on an "as is" basis. The author and publisher shall have neither liability nor responsibility to any person or entity with respect to any loss or damages arising from the information contained in this book or from the use of the procedures, programs, applications, equipment or devices mentioned in it.

Trademarks

All terms in this book that are known to be trademarks have been printed in initial capital letters or all capitals. The author and publisher of this book cannot attest to the accuracy of this information. Use of a term in this book should not be regarded as affecting the validity of any trademark or service mark.

Edited by Clarence Z. Seacrest

Illustrations by Frank McClain

Cover design by Prodesignsx

ISBN 978-0-9982384-8-7 (paperback)

About The Author

Frank McClain is a multi-award-winning author who graduated with a BS in Information Systems Management from the University of Maryland. He is a military veteran who served 20 years in the US Air Force both in the US and Europe. He lived and worked in Europe for over 12 years both as a US military member and as a civilian government contractor. He's worked over 15 years as an IT consultant in both US government and corporate jobs in the US and Europe.

Frank has extensive experience as a senior network engineer on IT production LAN, WAN and laboratory environments for many Fortune 500 companies and US government agencies. His experience includes researching, designing, drawing, documenting, procuring, configuring, installing, monitoring, troubleshooting and repairing a variety of networking components including routers, switches, firewalls, proxy web servers, multiplexers, modems, encryption gear and cabling.

Following are some of the US Department of Defense and other government agencies where Frank has either worked as a network engineer or provided IT support:

- Air Force
- Army
- Navy
- Marines
- Air Force Space Command (AFSPC)
- North American Aerospace Defense Command (NORAD)
- Missile Defense Agency (MDA)
- Defense Information Systems Agency (DISA)
- National Geospatial Intelligence Agency (NGA)
- Federal Bureau of Investigation (FBI)
- Central Intelligence Agency (CIA)
- National Security Agency (NSA)

Following are some of the European commercial service provider companies Frank has troubleshot networks with across Europe:

- Deutsche Telekom
- Telecom Italia
- Spain Telefonica

Following are some of the US commercial companies and clients Frank has worked for as a network engineer:

- Boeing
- Lockheed Martin
- SAIC
- Northrop Grumman
- Verizon
- Computer Sciences Corporation
- AECOM
- Telecommunications Systems
- Charter Communications
- ISYS Technologies
- PDS Technical Services
- NCI
- Insight Global
- SAP

Following are some of the IT certifications Frank has passed:

- CCNP
- CCNP Service Provider
- CCDP
- CCNA
- CCNA Security
- CCNA Voice
- CCNA Wireless
- CCNA Collaboration
- Cisco Video Network Specialist
- CCNA Data Center
- CCDA
- JNCIS-Service Provider
- JNCIS
- JNCIA-Junos
- MCP
- Security+
- Network+
- ITILv3

Dedication

To my Lord and Savior Jesus Christ.

"I know the plans I have for you", declares the LORD, *"plans to prosper you and not to harm you, plans to give you hope and a future."* Jeremiah 29:11 NIV

To all the colleagues and customers I've had the privilege and pleasure of working with and working for while engineering, implementing, monitoring, maintaining, troubleshooting and repairing your networks. This book is a culminating tribute to the time spent with you and your networks.

Thank you for the opportunity!

Table of Contents

Conventions and Command Syntax

- **Boldface** black font in a sentence indicates a command being explained, such as the **show interface** command in this sentence.

- Non-Boldface black font in a command indicates all command prompts, computer responses, and window screen tabs. For example: router(config)# is a prompt you will see for router commands; switch(config)# is a prompt you will see for switches; and so forth.

- **Boldface** font in a command indicates the portion you type in the command after the device prompt. For example: router(config)#**int Serial2/1**.

- | is a directive symbol, known as "pipe", in a command indicating separation of alternative choices. For example: **tunnel source** *<physical interface IP address | physical interface number | loopback IP address | loopback interface number>* **command**.

- < > is a directive symbol in a command indicating required arguments after a keyword. For example: router(config)#**int** *<interface>* is a directive symbol requiring you to type your selected interface. The *italics* indicates directive information you type in the command. Router(config)#**transport input** *<telnet | ssh | telnet ssh>* is a directive symbol requiring you to select one of the optional arguments. This directive symbol can contain other directive symbols in addition to keywords and arguments.

- [ ] is a directive symbol in a command indicating an optional keyword or argument. For example: router(config-line)#**exec-timeout** *<minutes>* [*seconds*] is a directive symbol requiring you to type your optional argument in seconds. Router(config)#**crypto key generate rsa** [**general-keys | usage-keys | signature | encryption**] is a directive symbol requiring you to select one of the argument options. This directive symbol can contain other directive symbols in addition to keywords and arguments.

- *<interface>* in a command indicates the media type, slot, port, and subinterface of an interface of a device. For example: router(config)#int *<interface>* could be typed as router(config)#int **Serial2/1** or router(config)#int **lo0** or router(config)#int **atm4/2.100.**

- *<physical interface number>* in a command indicates the media type, slot, and port of an interface of a device; but not the virtual interface or subinterface. For example: router(config)#int *<interface>* could be typed as router(config)#int **Ethernet3/1** or router(config)#int **Serial2/1.**

- *<subinterface number>* in a command indicates the virtual interface or subinterface number on a device. For example: **100** in the ATM interface **atm4/2.100** is the subinterface number.

- **Note:** provides additional instructions and background information.

- **Caution:** alerts you to important cautionary information to consider.

Icons Used in This Book

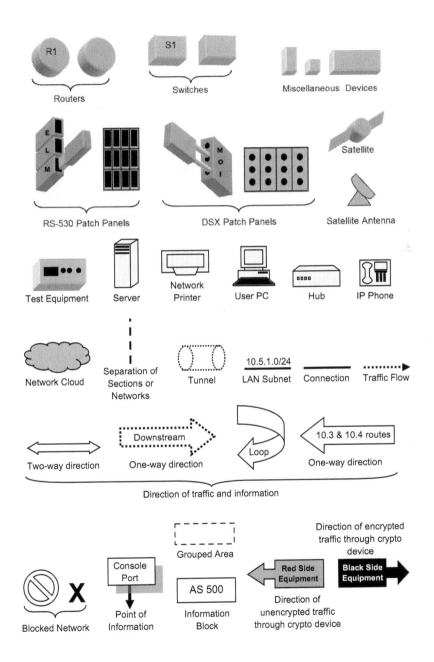

Routers

Switches

Miscellaneous Devices

RS-530 Patch Panels

DSX Patch Panels

Satellite

Satellite Antenna

Test Equipment

Server

Network Printer

User PC

Hub

IP Phone

Network Cloud

Separation of Sections or Networks

Tunnel

10.5.1.0/24
LAN Subnet

Connection

Traffic Flow

Two-way direction

Downstream
One-way direction

Loop

10.3 & 10.4 routes
One-way direction

Direction of traffic and information

Grouped Area

Direction of encrypted traffic through crypto device

Blocked Network

Console Port
Point of Information

AS 500
Information Block

Red Side Equipment

Black Side Equipment

Direction of unencrypted traffic through crypto device

Introduction

In 1965, Dr. Gordon E. Moore, co-founder of Intel Corporation and Fairchild Semiconductor, stated that the number of components (transistors) per integrated circuit (IC) would double every year; and in 1975, he updated his prediction by saying these micro-components would double every two years. Moore was right in his observations and predictions. Thanks to the realization of Dr. Moore's prediction, known as Moore's Law, the exponential growth of technology continues to be true for all of us in the 21st century.

Today, you have more computing power in your iPhone than NASA had in their computers when they first put a man on the moon in 1969. No one can keep pace with or knows everything about the ever-growing technology explosion. Oftentimes, like baby chicks in a bird's nest gobbling down mouthfuls at a time, we are preoccupied with feeding on vast amounts of information available and accessible to us today. Part of that nourishing information you need to help you grow wiser and stronger in your IT career is in this book.

Because of the ever-evolving and abounding IT information growth, you can only learn and digest so much from the best sources you can find about certain areas of IT as you pursue your career path. To help you with your journey through the IT industry, this book will help you navigate your way through your IT career by being one of your best sources on IT job interview questions and answers.

Who Should Read This Book

IT Questions & Answers For IT Job Interviews, Volume 1 is a guidebook for every IT professional. Whether you are an IT professional seeking work; IT interviewer who needs to ask the right questions to identify the right IT professional for the job; IT hiring manager who has to make the final decision on which IT candidate to hire; or IT recruiter having to locate candidates to fill IT positions, ***this book is for you***.

If you are an IT professional or someone seeking to be in the IT profession, this book is for you. *IT Interview Questions & Answers for IT Job Interviews* is the book job-seeking IT professionals have been waiting decades for someone to write. This book is a comprehensive quick reference IT job interview questions and answers guidebook for all IT professionals currently working in or are considering working in IT networking environments for private corporations or government organizations. If you want to ensure you are well-prepared for your next technical IT job interview, you need to read this book.

If you are a hiring manager or interviewer in the IT industry, this book is for you. IT professionals are busy people. When it comes to getting ready to interview several people for one or more available IT positions, let's face it: we're oftentimes scrambling to put questions together; we're looking for those same old worn-out questions we used last time; or we try to "wing it" hoping nobody will notice that we're not as prepared as we ought to be or like to be. Well those days are gone. This book is your quick reference toolbox from which you can select IT questions and answers quickly and easily that are currently being asked in today's IT industry.

If you are a recruiter in the IT industry, this book is for you. Are you overwhelmed by all the terms and acronyms used in the IT industry such as OSPF, EIGRP, BGP, MPLS, VoIP, TCP, SIP, VPN, VPLS, VRF, DWDM, EPON, QoS, STP, HSRP, NAT, ASA, multicast, access list (ACL), load balancer, LAN, WAN, optimization, virtualization, firewall, router, switch and server? This book is the friend you wish you had that can easily explain all of these IT terms and acronyms to you before you make that call or send that email to job candidates.

How This Book Will Help You

For **IT job seekers**, the IT job market is more competitive than ever; and those seeking a career in IT face heavy competition in reaching their desired position. Today's pool of IT professionals are better educated and more experienced and certified than previous generations. This book will provide you the IT questions and answers to beat out the competition and come out on top in the job interviewing, hiring and promotion process.

This book will provide you insight into the body of knowledge, devices, networks, configurations, and more importantly, actual IT interview questions and answers you need to know to perform well and stand out among other candidates in IT job interviews. If you've ever used IT questions and answers to help you pass IT certification exams, you know how valuable a tool that is. Think of the questions and answers in this book as your key to helping you pass your IT job interview exam.

Hiring managers and interviewers have been asking the questions in this book for years; and you can expect to be asked these same questions in your next IT technical interview too. Do yourself a favor and discover the questions constantly being asked in IT job interviews today.

The answers that come with every question in this book are accompanied by notes explaining further detail about the question and the answer; as well as charts and network diagrams that will give you a solid background and understanding of the subjects covered in each question.

Many of the insights on network commands, multi-vendor devices, applications and network diagrams shown in this book are what you may have seen or will see and work with in actual IT production and laboratory networks in many Fortune 500 businesses, service providers and government agencies today. Whether your focus is on routers, switches, firewalls, telepresence devices, WiFi, WAN optimizers, load balancers or other IT technologies, this book is an indispensable guide to what you need to know about these devices, networks, protocols, configurations and troubleshooting to help you pass your next IT job interview.

Do yourself a favor and find out what are the questions you will be asked in your next IT job interview—especially now that your hiring manager and other interviewers will be reading this book too.

For IT interviewers and hiring managers who performed interviews in the past or might become an IT interviewer in the future, you know the importance of having good, relevant IT technical questions and answers that will effectively identify the right IT professional in a job interview to join your team. No more scrambling to put together or print out questions and answers at the last minute when your manager informs you that you will join his or her interviewer panel. You'll be ready at a moment's notice with well-thought-out, professionally prepared IT questions that have been asked by many interviewers in the past for a variety of IT positions.

You're busy enough as it is on the job. That's why you need to hire another person. Why beat your head against the wall trying to reinvent the IT interview wheel when you don't have the time for that? Just pick out the questions from this book that relate to the IT position you seek to fill from the job candidates your team plans to interview. You'll recognize many of these questions that were either asked by you in past IT interviews or that you had to answer when you were being interviewed for IT jobs.

Of course, as a hiring manager or interviewer, you need more than just IT technical questions to determine the best candidate for the job. You also need to ask soft skill questions to evaluate the cultural fitness of candidates. That's why I wrote two award-winning books titled *The Ultimate Job Hunting Guidebook* and *YOU'RE HIRED!* to determine the quality of candidate's soft skills, emotional quotient and social skills that will make them a good team player in the workplace.

Lastly, **IT recruiters** are oftentimes bewildered by the multi-layered variety of IT jobs, responsibilities, equipment, terms and verbiage used in the IT world. It's no wonder that for many IT recruiters today, it's hit and miss when trying to match a job description with the skill sets of many IT professionals. This book is here to help you solve that puzzle of finding the right IT person to fit in the right IT job.

Finally! Someone who wrote a book to make your IT recruiting job easier. This book will arm you with something that will give you the power to propel you to the next level in your IT recruiting career—knowledge! The easy-to-read flow of information in this book will help you understand the actual verbiage and terms in so many IT job descriptions that made your eyes bleed. This information will help you talk more confidently and knowledgeably with IT professionals about a particular IT position you are trying to fill.

How This Book is Organized

IT Questions & Answers For IT Job Interviews, Volume 1 is organized in chapters, called sections, of questions and answers with accompanying notes. Each section of questions and answers is based on a particular IT subject such as general IT knowledge (OSI layer, best path determination, well-known port numbers, MTU and fragmentation, layer 2–4 header fields and data flow, DNS and ARP, router and switch basics); transmission lines and cabling; voice over IP (VoIP); video and telepresence over IP; and wireless LANs (WLANs).

These questions and answers cover a range of IT topics including multi-vendor devices, configurations, network architectures, troubleshooting and IT industry best practices.

Each section contains many frequently asked IT job interview questions currently being asked today by private corporations and government IT job interviewers. Each question is followed by the appropriate answer that IT interviewers expect you to give them.

Rather than provide you with only quick reference IT questions and answers that give you just enough information to make you dangerous on the job, these questions come with comprehensive explanations, notes, background information or charts about the IT subject being covered. This additional information will provide job seekers, interviewers and recruiters greater depth to their knowledge about each question and answer. To help reinforce your understanding of the IT subject, many of these questions come with network drawings to give you a visual picture of the network, devices or connectivity being covered.

To preserve the security of any actual network, only fictional IP addresses, Autonomous Service Numbers (ASN) and site locations are used throughout this book. No government or commercial classified information will be revealed in this book.

An *Appendix* at the end of this book provides you additional invaluable reference information you need to know to enhance your knowledge of networks used at private corporations and government organizations. This section includes information, tables and charts on a variety of IT and telecommunication subjects such as frequency spectrum chart, cable specifications, well-known port numbers, different administrative distances used by different vendor devices, IP address allocations, patch panel loopbacks, network device loopbacks and more.

SECTION ONE

General IT Knowledge Q&A

OSI LAYER Q&A

- **Question:** Explain the OSI model.
- **Same Question:** What are the 7 layers of the OSI model?
- **Answer:** The 7 layers of the OSI model are Application (layer 7), Presentation (layer 6), Session (layer 5), Transport (layer 4), Network (layer 3), Data Link (layer 2) and Physical (layer 1).

Note: Some people use mnemonic tricks to help them remember the seven Open Systems Interconnection (OSI) layers, such as "**A**ll **P**eople **S**eem **T**o **N**eed **D**ata **P**rocessing." The first letter in each word is the first letter for each OSI layer: A = Application Layer; P = Presentation Layer; S = Session Layer; T = Transport Layer; N = Network Layer; D = Data Link Layer; and P = Physical Layer. Following are examples of areas where each OSI layer is used:

- **Layer 7 – Application Layer:** Provides end users access to applications or processes used across networks. Other services the application layer provides are issuing port numbers, error handling and recovery, data flow, full process-to-process flow of application programs, and authentication between sender and receiver.

  Examples of the application layer are SIP, SSI, DNS, FTP, TFTP, SSH, Telnet, BOOTP, Gopher, HTTP, HTTPS, LDAP, NFS, NTP, DHCP, SMPP, SMTP, SNMP, SMPT, POP3, IMAP, RADIUS, FCIP, HL7, Modbus.

1

- **Layer 6 – Presentation Layer:** Translates data between the application layer and the network layer; and presents data to the application layer in an accurate, well-defined and standardized format or syntax for presentation to end devices and users. Other services the presentation layer provides are data encryption and decryption, character and string conversion, data compression and graphic handling. The presentation layer is sometimes referred to as the syntax layer.

  Examples of the presentation layer are MIME, Secure Socket Layer (SSL), TLS, XDR, TDI, ASCII, EBCDIC, MIDI, MPEG, JPEG, MP3.

- **Layer 5 – Session Layer:** Manages the setting up, maintaining and taking down (oftentimes called signaling) of the session connection between two end point application processes. These session connections are typically related to a particular port number from the application layer. The session layer is sometimes referred to as the port layer.

  Examples of the session layer are Sockets, Session Establishment, NetBIOS, NetBEUI, NFS, NCP, 9P, SAP, SMB, SOCKS, RPC.

- **Layer 4 – Transport Layer:** Translates (encapsulates and de-encapsulates) data between the upper layers (layers 5, 6 and 7) and the network layer. Transports the upper layers of data (from layers 5, 6 and 7 of the OSI model) from one host device to another host device. Two commonly used transport layer protocols are Transport Control Protocol (TCP) and User Datagram Protocol (UDP).

  TCP is a connection-oriented, reliable transport protocol that uses flow control (window sizing, sequencing and acknowledgements) as well as error detection and correction (through retransmission).

2

The term "connection-oriented" in TCP means TCP will open or establish a connection (through the 3-way handshake) first before sending the data to the remote end; and after the transmission is completed, TCP will close the connection.

UDP is a connectionless, unreliable transport protocol that does not use flow control (window sizing, sequencing and acknowledgements), error correction or retransmission (UDP uses a checksum to detect errors but it does not correct errors). Since UDP requires less processing than TCP, UDP is faster (less delay) than TCP. Therefore, UDP is the preferred transport protocol for delay-sensitive traffic such as VoIP and video over IP.

UDP is connectionless because it does not use flow control or error correction. The UDP header contains only 5 fields: source port, destination port, UDP length (so the receiving end knows when the layers 5–7 data begins), UDP checksum and data.

Examples of the transport layer are TCP, UDP, Stream Control Transmission Protocol (SCTP), Data Congestion Control Protocol (DCCP), Sequenced Packet Exchange (SPX), Authentication Header (AH), and Secure Socket Layer (SSL).

- **Layer 3 – Network Layer:** Translates (encapsulates and de-encapsulates) data between the transport layer (layer 4) and the data link layer (layer 2). Controls and manages the layer 3 addressing and routing of data across the network between end-point devices. Other services the network layer provides include encapsulating data into packets, fragmentation and reassembly of data, quality of service (QoS), authentication, route engineering, error handling, diagnostics and monitoring.

Examples of the network layer are routers, IP, IPX, IPsec, ESP, ICMP, IGMP, BGP, OSPF, EIGRP, RIP, IS-IS, GRE, Layer 3 VPNs.

- **Layer 2 – Data Link Layer:** Translates (encapsulates and de-encapsulates) data between the network layer and the physical layer (layer 1). Controls and manages the layer 2 addressing and transport of data across a physical link in a network. Also divides data into frames; and provides IP-to-MAC address resolution using ARP, error handling and class of service (CoS).

  Examples of the data link layer are switches, bridges, wireless access point (AP), network interface card (NIC), Ethernet, asynchronous transfer mode (ATM), fiber distributed data interface (FDDI), Frame Relay, high-level data link control (HDLC), inter-switch link (ISL), Token Ring, X.25, point-to-point protocol (PPP), Layer 2 Tunneling Protocol (L2TP), serial line Internet protocol (SLIP), Cisco Discovery Protocol (CDP), Address Resolution Protocol (ARP), virtual LAN (VLAN), Layer 2 VPNs and multi-protocol label switching (MPLS). Technically, MPLS resides between layers 2 and 3, and is oftentimes referred to as layer 2.5.

- **Layer 1 – Physical Layer:** Consists of the necessary transmission hardware needed to transmit the data through physical links and mediums between nodes across networking infrastructures end-to-end. Data is converted to streams of binary bits of ones and zeroes for transmission. Other services the physical layer provides include data rate, synchronization, transmission interface between devices and mediums, line configuration, topology design and transmission modes (such as half-duplex and full-duplex).

  Examples of the physical layer are repeaters, hubs, connectors, cabling, PhoneNet, plain old telephone system (POTS), public switched telephone network (PSTN), synchronous optical network (SONET)/synchronous digital hierarchy (SDH), optical transport network (OTN), digital subscriber line (DSL), integrated services digital network (ISDN), T1, USB and Bluetooth.

- **Question:** At what layer of the OSI model is a bridge and repeater?
- **Answer:** A bridge is a layer 2 (Data Link Layer) device. A repeater is a layer 1 (physical layer) device.

- **Question:** At what layer of the OSI model are ATM and SONET?
- **Answer:** ATM is used at layer 2 (Data Link Layer). SONET is used at layer 1 (Physical Layer).

BEST PATH DETERMINATION Q&A

- **Question:** What is the difference between administrative distance (AD) and the metrics used in routing.
- **Answer:** Administrative distance (AD) is used to determine which routing protocol to use when you have two or more different routing protocols to choose from—preference being given to the lowest AD.

   Routing protocol metrics relate to a single routing protocol so that once a routing protocol, such as BGP, is selected based on its AD value, the metrics used within BGP take over in determining which BGP route is the best path when you have several BGP routes to choose from to reach the same destination prefix.

Note: It's important to realize there is another factor that is considered first before the AD value and routing protocol metrics in determining the best path route. Routing decisions are first based on the most specific route, also referred to as a route with the longest prefix.

- **Question:** What is considered first in determining the best route?
- **Answer:** The most specific route, also referred to as a route with the longest prefix.

Note: The most specific route is a route that has the longest subnet mask, referred to as having the longest prefix. For example, the /28 bitmask

(255.255.255.240) is considered a longer prefix or more specific route (because it has more bits—28) than the /24 bitmask (255.255.255.0) which is considered a shorter prefix or less specific route (because it has fewer bits—24). Therefore, the /28 would be selected as the best route because it is considered a more specific route than /24 to the destination prefix. As you can see from the subnets and bitmasks in these examples, a longer prefix or more specific route has fewer (some people say narrower) host IP addresses than a shorter prefix or less specific route. The fewer or narrower the host IP addresses in the route, the more specific those IP addresses become.

The way a more specific route (longer prefix) affects route selection is that even though OSPF may have a better AD value (110) than external EIGRP (170), the external EIGRP route could be selected as the best route if it has a more specific route (longer prefix) than the OSPF route. For instance, let's say both an OSPF and EIGRP route to the same destination prefix exists in the IP routing table. The external EIGRP route has a more specific route (such as /28) to the same destination prefix as the OSPF route (such as /24). In this case, the external EIGRP route will be selected as the better route to the destination prefix.

A simple way to remember the longest prefix rule is to look for the route—among multiple routes to the same destination prefix—in the routing table that has the longest prefix or bitmask. For example, /28 bitmask is longer than /24; /24 bitmask is longer than /18; and /18 bitmask is longer than /8. The largest number is always the longest prefix; and the longest prefix always wins in route selection.

- **Question:** What is the administrative distance (AD) of a static route?
- **Answer:** A static route directed to a connected interface has an AD of zero (0). A static route directed to an IP address has an AD of one (1).

Note: Administrative distance is not always the same on different vendor devices. For examples, the AD of a static route can be either 0 or 1 on a Cisco device. On a Juniper device, a static route has an AD (called preference in Junos OS) of 5. On a Cisco device, eBGP has an AD of 20 and iBGP has an AD of 200. On Juniper or Alcatel-Lucent devices, BGP has an AD of 170. On a Cisco device, OSPF has an AD of 110. On Juniper or Alcatel-Lucent devices, OSPF-internal has an AD of 10 and OSPF-external has an AD of 150. See Appendix X, Y and Z for listings of all administrative distances for different vendor devices.

- **Question**: What is the administrative distance (AD) of eBGP and iBGP?
- **Answer**: eBGP has an AD of 20 and iBGP has an AD of 200.

- **Question**: You have an iBGP route and an OSPF route in the routing table for the same destination. Which route will be selected as the best path based on their administrative distances?
- **Answer**: The OSPF route.

Note: The AD for OSPF is 110. The AD for iBGP is 200. The smallest AD value is selected as the best path and placed in the IP routing table. Keep in mind that the route with longest prefix is considered first for selecting the best path before comparing administrative distances to determine the best path.

WELL-KNOWN PORT NUMBERS Q&A

- **Question**: What is SMTP and what port is it?
- **Answer**: Simple Mail Transfer Protocol (SMTP) is used for sending email, and uses TCP transport protocol on port 25.

Note: Either POPmail (TCP port 110) or IMAP4 (TCP port 143) are protocols used to receive email.

- **Question:** What port and transport protocol is FTP?
- **Answer:** Ports 20 and 21, and both ports use the TCP transport protocol.

Note: Port 20 is used for File Transport Protocol (FTP) data and port 21 is used for FTP control.

- **Question:** What port and transport protocol is HTTPS?
- **Answer:** Port 443 and uses the TCP transport protocol.

Note: HTTP uses port 80 and TCP transport protocol.

- **Question:** What port and transport protocol is SSH?
- **Answer:** Secure Shell (SSH) uses port 22 and the TCP transport protocol.

- **Question:** What port and transport protocol is Telnet?
- **Answer:** Port 23 and uses the TCP transport protocol.

- **Question:** What port and transport protocol is TACACS?
- **Answer:** Port 49 and uses both UDP and TCP transport protocols.

- **Question:** What port and transport protocol is DNS?
- **Answer:** Domain Name System (DNS) uses port 53 and both UDP and TCP transport protocols.

TCP HEADER Q&A

- **Question:** How long is a TCP header?
- **Answer:** 20 bytes (minimum) to 60 bytes (maximum).
- **Question:** Tell me as many of the fields in a TCP header that you know?
- **Answer:** Following are the fields in a TCP header:

Figure 1-1 *Transmission Control Protocol (TCP) header fields (20–60 bytes)*

Source port number (2 bytes)			Destination port number (2 bytes)	
Sequence number (4 bytes)				
Acknowledgement number (4 bytes)				
Data offset	Reserved	Control flags	Window size	
Checksum (2 bytes)			Urgent pointer (2 bytes)	
Optional data (0–40 bytes)				

- Source port number (2 bytes)

- Destination port number (2 bytes)

- Sequence number (4 bytes)

- Acknowledgement number (4 bytes)

- Data offset (4 bytes)

- Reserved (3 bits)

- Control flags (9 bits)

- Window size (2 bytes)

- Checksum (2 bytes)

- Urgent pointer (2 bytes)

- Optional data (0–40 bytes)

Note: Transport Control Protocol (TCP) is defined in RFC 793. TCP and UDP are part of the Transport Layer (layer 4) of the OSI model. The Transport Layer transports the upper layers of data (from layers 5, 6 and 7 of the OSI model) from one host device to another host. Oftentimes you see TCP/IP together which is simply a way of describing a suite of protocols that use TCP (layer 4) and IP (layer 3). A TCP segment consists of the TCP header and data (layers 5–7 data). Figure 1-1 shows the fields within a TCP header.

The layer 4 TCP segment (TCP header and layers 5–7 data it encapsulates) is located between the IP header and frame check sequence (FCS) of an IP datagram (packet) as shown in Figure 1-2. A packet is the layer 3 IP header and the segment it encapsulates. A frame is the layer 2 Datalink header and the packet it encapsulates. The entire combination of the headers and data (data is referred to as payload) that travels across a network is oftentimes referred to as a datagram or packet.

Figure 1-2 *Location of the TCP segment in a datagram or packet*

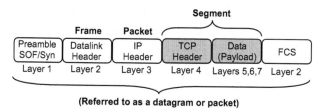

(Referred to as a datagram or packet)

- **Question:** What are the source and destination port numbers fields in the TCP header used for?
- **Answer:** The source port number identifies the application or service port number of the source host device. The destination port number identifies the application or service port number of the destination host device.

Note: For example, the source host could be a computer trying to access a website of a destination host such as a web server. In the TCP segment sent by the computer to the web server, the source port number would be a port number of the computer for this request; and the destination port number would be the well-known application port number for HTTP which is port 80 on the web server. Source and destination port numbers are also used in UDP.

The computer's source port number is used by the destination host (web server) to reply back to the correct port on the computer that sent the TCP segment request. The destination port number is used to identify the correct application or service (HTTP port 80) of the web server.

- **Question:** What is the data offset field in the TCP header used for?
- **Answer:** The data offset field, also referred to as the TCP header length, is used to tell the receiving end host device where the layers 5–7 data (payload) portion of TCP segment starts.

Note: The receiving host uses the value in the data offset field of the TCP header to calculate the number of bytes in the TCP header portion of the TCP segment. The resulting number of this calculation is the TCP header length (without the data portion) of the segment which the receiving host uses to determine where the data portion (the layers 5–7 data portion of each segment) begins. Without the TCP data offset number, the receiving host would not know where the TCP header ends and the data portion (layers 5, 6 and 7) begins in the TCP segment.

During the TCP 3-way handshake, there is no data in the layers 5–7 payload portion in the packets being exchanged between the two end hosts. The number in the data offset field is a hexadecimal number; and each hex character represents 4 binary bits (that's why the offset field is 4 bits). The number in the offset field is used in a calculation to provide you the TCP header length in bytes.

To calculate the TCP header length (in bytes) from the data offset number, multiply the data offset number by 32 and divide the result by 8. For example, if the data offset is 4, the TCP header length is (4 x 32)/8 = 16 bytes. Many definitions of the data offset field oftentimes seems confusing as people try to explain this field in terms of 32-bit multiples. Their confusing explanation is simply referring to this calculation I just explained to you.

Packet sniffers will actually perform this calculation for you when sniffing the TCP header; and provide you both the data offset value and the resulting TCP header length in bytes.

- **Question:** What is the control flags field in the TCP header used for?
- **Answer:** The control flags field identifies the purpose for the TCP segment and determines how the TCP segment will be treated by the receiving host.

Note: Examples of the types of flags used in the control flags field of the TCP header are SYN, ACK, FIN, Push and Reset flags. Any flag that is set with a 1 bit is turned on; and any flag that is set with a 0 bit is turned off. Since there are 9 bits in the control flags field, there can be a total of 9 different flags available in the TCP header.

- **Question:** Does TCP have error correction?
- **Answer:** Yes, the TCP header contains the Checksum field used for error-checking of the header and data (payload).

- **Question:** How does TCP establish a connection?
- **Same Question:** Explain the 3-way handshake in TCP?
- **Answer:** Transmission Control Protocol (TCP) uses a three-way handshake to establish a session connection between two hosts such as a client and server:

- First, the source host, such as a client computer, initiating the session will send a SYN (synchronize) packet that includes a segment sequence number and maximum segment size (MSS in bytes the sender wants to receive) to synchronize with the destination host such as a server. For example, the client sends a SYN packet with a sequence number of 2000 to the server.

- Second, the server will respond with a SYN-ACK packet to acknowledge (ACK) the client's SYN number and send back its own synchronize (SYN) number and MSS. The server will also increment the client's SYN segment sequence number by one in the server's ACK back to the client. For example, the server would respond back to the client with its own SYN sequence number of 3000 along with an ACK number of 2001 (2000 + 1).

- Third, the client will send an ACK packet to acknowledge the server's SYN request by incrementing the server's SYN sequence number by one in the ACK back to the server. The client will include its own incremented sequence number. For example, the client will respond back to the server with the same sequence number of 2001 and an ACK number of 3001 (3000 + 1).

Note: The SYN (synchronize), ACK (acknowledge), FIN (final), RST (reset), PSH (push) and URG (urgent) flags are located in the Control flags field of the TCP header. The TCP connection (session) termination is a four-way handshake that uses FIN, ACK, FIN, ACK between the two end hosts to close their connection.

A half-open TCP connection is when one end has terminated their connection while the other end's TCP connection is still open. Multiple half-open TCP connections are what an attacker uses in what's called a SYN flood attack, a type of denial of service (DoS) or distributed denial of service (DDoS) attack against network servers. With a TCP SYN flood attack, the attacker will send multiple SYN requests with fake source IP addresses to all the ports of a server. The server will respond from each of its open TCP ports to all of these SYN requests with SYN/ACK replies; and then wait for the final ACK replies in the three-way handshake. However, the attacker will not respond with the final ACK replies. Since the fake source IP addresses appear legit, the server does not close these false connections with a reset (RST) packet; therefore, all of the server's ports remain open and occupied while waiting for the ACK replies from the attacking device. As a result, the server's resources become unavailable to legitimate users because all of the server's TCP ports are in use—thus the phrase "denial of service".

■ **Question:** What is maximum segment size (MSS)?
■ **Answer:** Maximum segment size sets the maximum size of data within each TCP segment that can be sent to the receiving device.

Note: The maximum segment size (MSS) is the size of data (minus the TCP header) within each TCP segment that devices will use when sending TCP segments to receiving devices. The default MSS is 536 bytes. Although the varying sliding window size from the receiving device determines how much data the sending device will put into each TCP segment that is sent at any given moment, that data can never exceed the MSS. The MSS refers only to the data within each TCP segment; it does not include the TCP header. The default TCP header size is 20 bytes without the use of TCP options which will increase TCP header size beyond 20 bytes. Therefore, if the MSS of the data is 400 bytes, the "actual" maximum size of the TCP segment would be 420 bytes that includes the default 20-byte TCP header. If the "actual" maximum segment size (TCP header and data) is too large, it can increase the size of the layer 3 IP datagram (packet) that encapsulates the layer 4 TCP segment. This may cause the larger IP packet to be fragmented by an interface's MTU (maximum transmission unit) size limitations. As a result of fragmentation, part of the TCP segment within that fragmented IP packet may also be fragmented; however, the segment is reassembled (without knowing) when the IP packet is reassembled.

As a precaution against fragmentation, the default MSS of each TCP segment is set to 536 bytes which takes into account a default 20-byte TCP header and default 20-byte IP header for a total 576-byte IP packet as the minimum MTU that all IP networks will allow without fragmenting (RFC 791). Any TCP or IP options used will increase the total minimum MTU size of 576 bytes to a larger size IP packet.

During the TCP 3-way handshake between two devices establishing a connection, both end devices can use the Maximum Segment Size TCP option in its SYN message of the handshake to specify an MSS size that is either larger or smaller than the default 536-byte MSS it wants to receive from the sending device. Therefore, each sending device could be using a different MSS size based on what the receiving device wants to receive.

Path MTU Discovery (PMTUD) is used by each end device to determine whether the IP network will allow larger or smaller size IP packets before fragmenting those packets. This in turn will help each end device to either increase or decrease their desired MSS size they want to receive, to prevent fragmentation, based on what the MTUs of devices along the IP network path will allow.

- **Question:** What is the more aggressive mode of TCP?
- **Answer:** A more aggressive mode of standard TCP is High-Speed TCP (HS-TCP) that allows HS-TCP's window size to grow faster than standard TCP in addition to recover from packet loss quicker.

Note: In 1981, RFC 793 defined Transport Control Protocol. You can use a more aggressive mode of TCP, called high-speed TCP (HS-TCP), that was introduced in 2003 in RFC 3649 for WAN links that require higher bandwidth throughput (over 50Mbps); experience high latency; and are used with quality of service (QoS) classifications and satellite links.

HS-TCP modifies the congestion control mechanism of standard TCP to allow for faster responses to congestion on the network, particularly large WAN networks that oftentimes experience delay issues that cause problems for standard TCP.

There are many vendor devices on the market that seek to counter the effects of delay on the WAN network. For example, the Riverbed SteelHead WAN optimization device can also use Riverbed's proprietary maximum TCP (MX-TCP) feature which is an even more aggressive form of TCP than HS-TCP. MX-TCP ignores the congestion control mechanism used by TCP while HS-TCP still follows this mechanism.

- **Question:** What is the difference between TCP and UDP?
- **Answer:** Following are the differences between TCP and UDP:

  - **Transmission Control Protocol (TCP)** is a connection-oriented protocol that provides reliability, sequence ordering and error-checking of packets from source to destination. The receiving end will check for complete and accurate data transmission. If the data packet is corrupt or missing at the receiving end, it will drop the packet; notify the sending device; and the source transmitting end will resend the data.

  - **User Datagram Protocol (UDP)** is a connectionless protocol. No error checking is provided with UDP; therefore, it is a best-effort protocol. Since there is less processing required for UDP than TCP, UDP is faster than TCP.

Note: TCP is a connection-oriented, reliable transport protocol that uses flow control (window sizing, sequencing and acknowledgements) as well as error detection and correction (through retransmission).

The term "connection-oriented" in TCP means TCP will open or establish a connection (through the 3-way handshake) between two end hosts first before sending the payload (voice, video or data) between the two end hosts; and after the transmission is completed, TCP will close the connection.

TCP is used for applications that require high reliability and proper ordering of packets where transmission time (delay) is less critical. Applications such as FTP, SSH, Telnet, SMTP, HTTTP and HTTPS use TCP. Protocols such as DNS and TACACS can use both TCP and UDP.

UDP is connectionless because it does not open or establish a connection first before sending the payload; and does not use flow control features or error correction. The UDP header contains only 5 fields: source port, destination port, UDP length (so the receiving end knows when the layers 5–7 data begins), UDP checksum and data.

Although UDP uses a checksum, data corruption is possible because UDP can detect errors but it does not correct errors. Since UDP requires less processing than TCP, UDP is faster (less delay) than TCP. Therefore, UDP is the preferred transport protocol for delay-sensitive traffic such as VoIP and video over IP.

The UDP protocol is used for applications that require faster transmission speeds with less delay that do not require proper sequencing of packets and that can handle some packet loss. Applications such as DHCP, TFTP, SNMP, RIP, VoIP and video over IP use UDP. Although it is best to use UDP for live video streaming, you could use TCP for recorded video.

MTU AND FRAGMENTATION Q&A

- **Question:** What is MTU?

- **Answer:** The maximum transmission unit (MTU) defines the maximum size, in bytes, of a layer 3 packet that is allowed to transit over an interface without fragmentation. The minimum MTU default is 576 bytes but Cisco typically uses a default 1500 bytes.

Note: A protocol data unit (PDU) is a unit of measure for data at each OSI layer, such as a segment at layer 4, a packet at layer 3 or a frame at layer 2. The MTU is typically 1500 bytes by default on some Cisco router and switch interfaces. The default MTU size of a packet can vary based on the media type, device or vendor. MTU can also mean multi-tenant unit (MTU) switch used in Virtual Private LAN Service (VPLS) explained in Service Provider Networks Questions and Answers section of volume 6.

- **Question:** Explain fragmentation?
- **Answer:** IP fragmentation occurs at an interface to break down or fragment a layer 3 IP packet to a size allowed by the interface's maximum transmission unit (MTU) setting to ensure the packet will be supported by IP networks from source host to destination host.

Note: A packet is oftentimes referred to as a datagram. A packet or datagram is a self-contained layer 3 protocol data unit (PDU) containing header and payload (data) sections used to route information, video and voice data from source to destination across a packet-switched (IP) network. The self-contained information in the header of the datagram (packet) allows each IP packet to use connectionless communication across networks instead of connection-oriented communication.

Devices will not fragment the default minimum IP packet size of 576 bytes (RFC 791). The maximum packet size is 65,535 bytes. Device interfaces limit the size of bytes allowed for each IP packet based on the MTU setting on the interface. When fragmentation occurs, it means there is an MTU mismatch between network devices somewhere on the end-to-end path. Fragmentation slightly increases CPU utilization and memory usage on all end-to-end devices performing the fragmentation.

Packets from source hosts may have a larger MTU size than MTU settings on the interfaces of intermediate devices along the IP network path. When this occurs, the device's interface will fragment the packet before transmitting the packet to the destination address. Routers may fragment packets but they don't reassemble fragmented packets—that's the job of the receiving host device such as a desktop computer. If one of the fragmented packets are lost or corrupted, that entire packet must be resent by the source device. One important reason why endpoint routers do not reassemble fragmented packets is because IP packets can take an asymmetric route where any endpoint router may not see all of the fragmented packets of the original IP packet. Another reason endpoint routers do not reassemble fragmented IP packets is due to the increased delay and overhead required to buffer and process the arrival of all fragmented packets.

Fragmentation is usually on by default on Cisco routers. Fragmentation can be turned on with a 1-bit (may fragment) or off with a 0-bit (don't fragment—DF, referred to as the DF-bit) in the Flags field of the IP header. Use the **set ip df <0 | 1>** command in a route map to set the DF-bit.

Firewalls may experience difficulty recognizing the fragmented packet, and as a result, block the fragmented packet.

- **Question:** What is PMTUD?
- **Answer:** Path MTU Discovery (PMTUD) uses ICMP to help source routers dynamically learn the MTU settings of other devices along the end-to-end path in order to prevent fragmentation of IP packets.

Note: RFC 1191 defines PMTUD for IPv4 traffic. RFC 1981 defines PMTUD for IPv6 traffic. PMTUD is only supported by TCP. Since MTU settings on devices along the path are not dynamically discovered by the local routers at both ends of the path, PMTUD can be enabled on source routers at both ends using the ip tcp path-mtu-discovery global configuration command on Cisco routers. The PMTUD command sets the "don't fragment" (DF) flag in the IP header of each packet coming from the source that prevents fragmentation by routers along the end-to-end path.

With PMTUD turned on, the source router will send a TCP IP datagram (packet) using its own MTU size. When devices along the path receive the TCP packet with the DF (don't fragment) o-bit set in the Flags field in the IP header, and this IP packet is larger than that device's interface MTU setting, the device will drop this packet (instead of fragmenting it) and send an ICMP "Fragmentation Needed and DF set" (Type 3, Code 4) unreachable message containing its interface MTU size back to the source router. The source router will reduce its TCP maximum segment size (MSS) of each TCP segment that is encapsulated within IP packets. This reduces the total size of IP packets from the source router to match the MTU of that device on the path that sent the ICMP message.

In order for PMTUD to work properly, it is important for routers to not rate-limit this special PMTUD ICMP unreachable message and for firewalls to not filter the PMTUD ICMP (Type 3, Code 4) message. You may be able to avoid the router rate-limiting or firewall filtering issue by adjusting the maximum segment size (MSS) with the ip tcp adjust-mss <value> interface configuration command on the Cisco source router. This command will adjust the special TCP optional MSS in each TCP segment to a value equal to the minimum MTU that endpoint devices will accept on their interfaces. As a result, both endpoint devices are tricked into thinking the MSS value is lower than it actually is.

The ip tcp path-mtu-discovery global configuration command along with the ip tcp adjust-mss <value> interface configuration command are commonly used for VPN solutions, such as MPLS, IPsec, GRE and DMVPN tunnels, to overcome fragmentation issues when using VPNs.

If PMTUD is turned off while the DF-bit is set to on, routers along the path will discard packet sizes larger that their MTU interface settings but will not send an ICMP "Fragmentation Needed and DF set" message back to the source router. As a result, local hosts will experience poor performance such as poor upload or download capabilities of TCP applications across the network end-to-end.

TCP MSS is also used between hosts at both ends during the 3-way handshake to determine the proper size of TCP/IP datagrams that both ends will use in transmission to properly communicate with each other without fragmenting the IP packets across IP networks.

PMTUD is also enabled by default on all BGP neighbor sessions on Cisco routers and can be disabled globally with the **no bgp transport path-mtu-discovery** global configuration command. PMTUD can be disabled for one BGP neighbor with the **no neighbor** *<neighbor IP address>* **transport path-mtu-discovery** router address-family configuration command (for IOS) or the **neighbor** *<neighbor IP address>* **transport path-mtu-discovery disable** router address-family configuration command (for IOS-XE).

- **Question:** With PMTUD turned on, when routers along the path receive TCP packets with the DF (don't fragment) 0-bit set in the IP header, and these packets are larger than that router's interface MTU setting, the router will drop these packets (instead of fragmenting them) and send an ICMP "Fragmentation Needed and DF set" unreachable message back to the source router. What is this ICMP code for PMTUD?
- **Answer:** Type 3, Code 4

Note: The ICMP Type 3 is the "Destination Unreachable"; and the ICMP Code 4 is "Fragmentation Needed and Don't Fragment was Set". IPv6 supports PMTUD; however, IPv6 does not support fragmentation of the Don't Fragment option. Therefore, when an IPv6 interface receives a packet larger than the MTU on the interface, IPv6 will drop the packet and send an ICMPv6 Packet Too Big (Type 2) message containing its interface MTU size back to the source host. ICMPv6 is defined in RFC 4443.

- **Question:** What other transport protocols are used with PMTUD?
- **Answer:** Only TCP supports PMTUD.

IPv4 HEADER Q&A

- **Question:** How long is an IPv4 header?
- **Answer:** 20 bytes (minimum) to 60 bytes (maximum).

- **Question:** Tell me as many of the fields in a IPv4 header that you know?
- **Answer:** Following are the fields in a IPv4 header:

Figure 1-2 *IPv4 header fields*

Version (4 bits)	Header Length (4 bits)	Type of Service (8 bits)	Total Lengths (16 bits)		
Identification (16 bits)	(0 bit)	DF (1 bit)	MF (1 bit)	Fragment Offset (13 bits)	
Time to live (8 bits)	Protocol (8 bits)		Header checksum (16 bits)		
Source IP Address (32 bits)					
Destination IP Address (32 bits)					
Options (0–40 bytes					
Data					

- **Version (4 bits):** Defines either version 4 or 6 of IP.

- **Internet Header Length (IHL) (4 bits):** Defines the total header length including the Internet (IP or Internet Protocol) header which is 20 bytes (minimum) to 60 bytes (maximum when options are used). IHL does not include the data (payload). This field along with the Total Length field tells the receiving end host device where the IP header ends and the layers 5–7 data (payload) portion of IP packet starts.

- **Type of Service (8 bits):** Identifies the Differentiated Service Code Point (DSCP) or IP Precedence (IPP) value used in QoS marking.

- **Explicit Congestion Notification (ECN) (2 bits):** Allows the receiving device to notify the sending device of any network congestion end-to-end without dropping packets which would normally be dropped without ECN enabled. In order for ECN to work, the network must support it and endpoint devices must be enabled with it.

- **Total Length (16 bits):** Defines the total length of the IP datagram including the IP header and the data (payload) which is 1 byte (minimum) to 65,535 bytes (maximum). This field along with the IHL field tells the receiving end host device where the IP header ends and the layers 5–7 data (payload) portion of IP packet starts. The Total Length value minus the Header Length value identifies where the IP header ends and the payload begins.

- **Identification (16 bits):** Used to uniquely identify each IP packet sent by the source host so the receiving host can reassemble fragmented IP packets. All fragments of the same single IP packet will use the same identification value.

- **Flags (3 bits):** The first bit of the 3 bits is reserved (0) and not used. The second bit is used to represent the **DF** (Don't Fragment) bit. A 1-bit DF means "don't fragment"; a 0-bit DF means "fragment". The third bit **MF** (More Fragments) is used to indicate if the next packet is fragmented or not. A 1-bit MF means there are more fragmented packets enroute for a specific IP packet before reassembly can begin; a 0-bit MF means this is the last fragmented packet for a specific IP packet.

- **Fragment offset (13 bits):** Helps in reassembly of fragmented packets by identifying each fragment packet position to properly reassemble a specific original IP packet sent by the source device because fragments can arrive at their destination out of order.

- **Time to live (TTL) (8 bits):** Indicates the number of hops allowed before the packet is discarded (to prevent routing loops).

- **Protocol (8 bits):** Identifies the layer 4 protocol as TCP or UDP.

- **Header checksum (16 bits):** Uses a resulting value that was calculated using an algorithm of all the fields in the IP header to ensure the receiving host has the same value as the sending host.

- **Source IP address (32 bits):** Contains the IP address of the sending host.

- **Destination IP address (32 bits):** Contains the IP address of the receiving host.

- **Options (0–40 bits):** Each option is a multiple of 32 bits. If the option is less than 32 bits, a Padding is added to increase the option to 32 bits. Using options increases the size of IP packets.

- **Data:** Contains the upper layer data (layers 5–7 payload).

■ **Question:** What is DSCP used for in an IPv4 header?
■ **Answer:** Quality of Service (QoS) marking.

FRAME HEADER Q&A

■ **Question:** Tell as many of the fields you know in a frame header?

■ **Answer:** Following are the fields in a frame header:

Figure 1-3 *Ethernet frame header fields*

Preamble (7 bits)	Start Frame Delimiter (1 byte)	Destination Address (6 bytes)	Source Address (6 bytes)	Length (2 bytes)	Data (40–1500 bytes)	Frame Check Sequence (CRC) (4 bytes)

- Preamble (7 bytes)

- Start of frame delimiter (1 byte)

- MAC Destination address (6 bytes)

- MAC Source address (6 bytes)

- 802.1Q tag (optional for VLANs) (4 bytes)

- Ethertype or Length (2 bytes): The EtherType code indicates the type of frame, such as Ethernet, Token Ring, FDDI or ATM frame. The Length code identifies what higher-level protocol, such as TCP or UDP, is being carried in the frame.

- Logical Link Control (LLC) (optional 3 or 8 bytes)

- Data (Payload) (46–1500 bytes)

- Pad: To meet the 64 bytes requirement of an IEEE 802.3 Ethernet frame, padding is used to add zero bytes to Ethernet frames that are less than 64 bytes long to reach the 64 bytes minimum size limit. Ethernet Frames less than 64 bytes will be dropped by the receiving end.

- Frame check sequence (CRC) (4 bytes)

- **Question:** How long is an Ethernet frame?
- **Answer:** The size of the IEEE 802.3 Ethernet frame is 64 bytes (minimum) to 1522 bytes (maximum).

Note: The maximum size of the original IEEE 802.3 Ethernet frame was 1518 bytes. To accommodate IEEE 802.1Q VLAN tagging, the Ethernet frame was increased to 1522 bytes. If an Ethernet frame carries an ICMP packet, its minimum size increased from 64 bytes to 74 bytes. The maximum frame size ultimately depends on the maximum transmission unit (MTU) on the interface. The default MTU size on many interfaces is 1500 bytes.

- **Question:** How long is an Ethernet header?
- **Answer:** 18 bytes.

DNS AND ARP Q&A

- **Question:** Explain how DNS works?
- **Answer:** The Domain Name System (DNS) is used to resolve domain names and translate them to IP addresses. When you type a name in the web browser of your PC, such as www.cisco.com to reach the Cisco website, your computer's DNS cache or your company's DNS server or the service provider's DNS server will resolve (translate) the www.cisco.com web name to a routable IP address, such as 23.79.213.27, that all devices on the network understand and communicate with in order to send packets with that IP address to the proper devices on the network to reach the target destination.

Note: The reason we type names of websites instead of IP address in the browser window is because names are easier to remember than numbers (IP addresses) representing the destination we want to reach.

When someone types in a website name, such as www.cisco.com, on their computer's web browser, the browser will check its DNS cache of their local computer to see if it has an IP address associated with that website name. If it does, the browser will use that IP address as the destination IP address for the web server. If it does not know the IP address, it will request a DNS name resolution (called a DNS query) from its assigned DNS server (called a recursive DNS server) to obtain the IP address for that website name. Typically, your workplace's local network or an Internet service provider will assign your computer a DNS server that handles the mapping of host names to IP addresses.

Typically, the recursive DNS server will have the IP address for your requested host name in its DNS cache; and will reply back to your computer with that IP address. If the recursive DNS server does not have that IP address in its DNS cache, it will ask (DNS query) a root name server, also referred to as root servers or the authoritative name server.

There are 13 root name servers that oversee the DNS root zone, a network of hundreds of servers in many countries worldwide. The root zone was created by the Internet Assigned Numbers Authority (IANA). Root name servers can make DNS requests to Top-Level Domain (TLD) name servers within the DNS root zone to find out (resolve) the IP address of your requested host name. Examples of Top-Level Domains are .com, .org and .gov.

Once the root name server receives a reply from a TLD name server about the IP address for your host name, it will relay this IP address back to the recursive DNS server, which in turn will reply back to your computer with this IP address.
IANA is part of the Internet Corporation for Assigned Names and Numbers (ICANN). ICANN is the organization that controls and manages the name and number systems of the Internet. ICANN provides accreditation to domain name registrars that delegate to users, companies and service providers (ISPs) the right to use a domain name on the Internet.

Each registry is an organization that manages and controls the registration of domain names with their respective domains. Each domain name registry provides their domain name registration information to other authorized domain name registries.

- **Question:** Explain how ARP works?
- **Answer:** The Address Resolution Protocol (ARP) is a layer 2 protocol used to map an IP address to a device's unique MAC address on a LAN. When a device receives a packet with a destination IP address, the device will look in its ARP cache (for computers) or MAC table (for switches) for the corresponding MAC address for that IP address. If there is an IP-to-MAC address match in its ARP cache (or MAC table), the device will forward the packet to the destination device on the LAN matching that MAC address.

  If the ARP cache (or MAC table) does not contain a matching MAC address, the device will broadcast an ARP request message to all devices on the LAN to see if a device on the network will respond back with a unicast ARP reply message that contains the matching MAC address for that IP address.

  In the case of a switch, it will broadcast an ARP request message out of all its ports within the same VLAN as the port where the switch received the frame (or ARP request). However, it will not broadcast an ARP request message out of the port where the switch received the frame (or ARP request)—this prevents routing loops.

  When the device that initially broadcasted the ARP request receives the unicast ARP reply, that device will update its ARP cache (or MAC table) and forward the packet out the port to the device that responded with the ARP reply message. Additionally, the responding device will update its own ARP cache (or MAC table) if it did not already have the broadcasting device's IP-to-MAC address in its own

ARP cache (or MAC table). If no device responds to the ARP request, the device that sent the ARP broadcast will drop the packet.

Note: RFC 826 defines ARP for Ethernet that uses a 48-bit Ethernet address. Devices hold an ARP table, also known as ARP cache, that lists the IP address-to-MAC address mapping.

When a device broadcasts the ARP request message across the LAN, the devices is basically asking, "*Who is IP address x.x.x.x?*", such as "*Who is IP address 192.168.10.2?*". The device responding back is basically saying, "*I am (the path to) IP address 192.168.10.2*".

The ARP request message being broadcasted will include the broadcasting device's IP address and MAC address in addition to the IP address for which the device is looking for the matching MAC address.

PACKET FLOW Q&A

■ **Question:** Describe how a data packet travels from a host through a switch and router to another host.
■ **Answer:** Following is how a host computer initiates and establishes communications with a host server. We'll use the example of a person using a computer to access a web server.

Note: Explaining this answer could take 2–5 minutes depending on how long it takes you to explain this process. Figure 1-4 will be used to help you visualize how data flows through the TCP/IP model from the computer host to the web server host.

Figure 1-4 *TCP/IP model data flow from computer to web server*

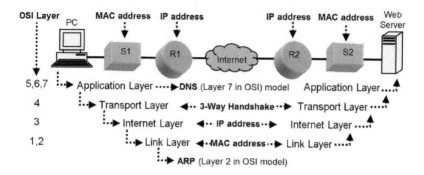

- Using the TCP/IP model (instead of the OSI model), data flows from the Application Layer; to the Transport Layer; to the Internet Layer; and then to the Link Layer at the source host computer; and then in the reverse order at the destination host server.

On the host computer side (Local end)

- When a user types in the website name in the web browser of their computer, the Application Layer uses the HTTP application to find the right port number for that application (which is port 80 for HTTP). The HTTP application port 80 web request is sent to the Transport Layer.

Note: When someone types in a website name, such as www.cisco.com, on their computer's web browser, the browser will check its DNS cache on the computer to see if it has an IP address associated with that website name. If it does, the browser will use that IP address as the destination IP address for the web server. If it does not know the IP address, it will request a DNS name resolution (called a DNS query) from its assigned DNS server (called a recursive DNS server) to obtain the IP address for that website name. Typically, your workplace network or Internet service provider will assign your computer a DNS server that handles the mapping of host names to IP addresses.

- The **Transport Layer** adds the proper transport protocol (which is TCP for HTTP) with source port number (the local computer's port number) and destination port number (port 80) for the HTTP request. It is also the TCP Transport Layer that starts a SYN (synchronize) packet to initiate a 3-way handshake with the web server at the remote end. TCP also divides all Application Layer data (datagrams) into segments and arranges those segments in the correct order. The Transport Layer encapsulates each segment of data and sends it to the Internet Layer.

Note: The client (computer) and server (HTTP web server) will use TCP to perform the 3-way handshake (SYN, SYN ACK, ACK) to establish a TCP communications session. During the 3-way handshake, both the client and server will establish the Maximum Segment Size (MSS) of each packet to prevent fragmentation of each packet in transit.

- The **Internet Layer** (called the Network Layer in the OSI model) provides each segment with the source IP address of the local computer and the destination IP address of the remote web server so each packet can be routed across the network. The Internet Layer encapsulates each segment with an IP header. The Internet Layer will then send each packet to the Link Layer.

Note: The source IP address is the computer's IP address that is assigned to it either manually or through a DNS server. In the Application layer, the computer host resolved the website name to the destination IP address using either its own DNS cache or received the name resolution from a DNS server. It is this destination IP address that is used as the destination address in the IP header of each packet at the Internet Layer.

- The **Link Layer** (called the Data Link Layer and Physical Layer in the OSI model) will add a source and destination MAC address to each packet and encapsulate each packet with a frame header. The Link Layer will send the frame to the switch.

Note: The **Data Link Layer** (OSI model) portion of the Link Layer (TCP/IP model) looks in its computer ARP cache for the corresponding MAC address for that destination IP address. If the computer does not have a MAC address that matches that IP address in its ARP cache, it will broadcast an ARP request message to the switch it is connected to in order to ask for the MAC address to reach that IP address.

The **Physical Layer** (OSI model) portion of the Link Layer (TCP/IP model) converts each frame into an electrical signal (for copper wired network) or light signal (for fiber wired network) or radio signal (for wireless network); and passes the frame to a switch (S1 in Figure 1-4).

- The **switch** receives the frame from the computer; looks in its MAC table for a matching outgoing interface for the destination MAC address shown in the received frame header; changes the destination MAC address to the MAC address of next-hop device's interface (router R1's interface in our example in Figure 1-4) and forwards the frame out the proper interface toward that next-hop device (router R1 in Figure 1-4).

- When the frame reaches the **router** (R1 in Figure 1-4), the router will look at the destination IP address in the packet's IP header; look in its IP routing table for the next hop for that destination IP address; and forwards (routes) that packet out the appropriate outgoing interface across the Internet to the HTTP web server.

On the server side (Remote end)

- The **router** (R2 in Figure 1-4) receives the packet from the Internet; looks at the frame header (for layer 2 switching) or the IP header (for layer 3 routing if more routers are involved); and forwards the packet to switch S2 on the web server's remote end as shown in Figure 1-4.

- The **switch** (S2 in Figure 1-4) looks at the destination MAC address in the frame; looks up the destination MAC in its MAC table to find the outgoing interface for that frame; changes the destination MAC to the web server's MAC address; and forwards the frame out its port to the web server.

- The web server receives the packet on its **Link Layer**; removes the frame header (layer 2) to reveal the source and destination IP address (layer 3) and passes the packet to the Internet Layer.

- The **Internet Layer** removes the IP header to reveal the TCP transport segment (layer 4) and passes the segment to the Transport Layer.

- The **Transport Layer** looks at the TCP port number 80 segment; knows it is an HTTP application request; and passes the HTTP application request to the **Application Layer** of the web server for processing.

BASIC ROUTING AND SWITCHING Q&A

- **Question:** What is the difference between a router, switch and hub?
- **Answer:** Following are the differences between a router, switch and hub:

- A **router** works at layer 3 (Network Layer) of the OSI model and provides separation between collision domains and separation between broadcast domains.

- **Switches** work at layer 2 (Data Link Layer) of the OSI model and perform separation between collision domains only. However, a switch configured with VLANs can also provide separation between broadcast domains of each VLAN.

- A **hub** operates at layer 1 (Physical Layer) of the OSI model and does not provide separation for either broadcast or collision domains.

■ **Question:** What is the difference between a control plane, data plane and management plane?

■ **Answer:** The **control plane** handles or controls all routing of layer 3 protocol traffic (such as BGP, OSPF, IS-IS or EIGRP) or all switching of layer 2 protocols (such as VTP, VLANs, CDP or STP) flowing to or from the device. The **data plane** handles all the data traffic transiting through the device. The **management plane** allows you to manage and monitor the device either locally or remotely.

Note: The control plane and management plane are all typically located on the devices supervisor card. The control plane typically uses software to control the routing or switching of traffic to and from the device. The data plane typically uses application-specific integrated circuits (ASICs) in hardware to control traffic flowing from one inbound interface to another outbound interface.

■ **Question:** What does Cisco devices use to discover the identity and capabilities of other Cisco devices on the network, and what is the CLI command used to identify these Cisco devices?

- **Answer:** Cisco devices use Cisco Discovery Protocol (CDP) to discover the identity and capabilities of other directly-connected Cisco devices. From a Cisco device, use the **show cdp neighbor** or **show cdp neighbor details** commands to view the identity and capabilities of other directly-connected Cisco devices.

Note: CDP cannot discover the identity and capabilities of devices that are not directly-connected. CDP can be turned off on a Cisco device, in which case, you or a Cisco device would not be able to discover the identity or capabilities of other Cisco devices that have CDP turned off. Some organizations will turn off CDP on some devices as a security practice.

CDP is Cisco proprietary and is not used in other vendor devices, such as Juniper or Alcatel-Lucent devices. These non-Cisco vendors use Link Layer Discovery Protocol (LLDP) on their non-Cisco devices to enable them to discover the identity and capabilities of other directly connected non-Cisco devices on the network. LLDP was formally known as Station and Media Access Control Connectivity Discovery and is defined in IEEE 802.1AB.

For non-Cisco devices, use the **show lldp neighbor** or **show lldp neighbor details** commands to view the identity and capabilities of other directly-connected non-Cisco devices.

- **Question:** Explain the two types of hypervisors?
- **Answer:** The two types of hypervisors are Type 1 and Type 2 hypervisors. In Type 1, called bare-metal hypervisor, the hypervisor runs directly on the system hardware. In Type 2, the hypervisor runs on a host operating system of the system hardware.

Note: Hypervisors allow you to virtualize a single physical device into multiple virtual devices called virtual machines (VMs) or virtual machine monitor. The VMs will share the CPU processors, memory, disk and other resources on the physical device and outside resources used by the physical device such as the power source, cabling and network infrastructure.

Examples of Type 1 hypervisors that run directly on the system hardware are VMware vSphere/ESXi, Microsoft Hyper-V, Kernel-Based Virtual Machine (KVM), Red Hat Enterprise Virtualization (RHEV) and Xen/Citrix ExnServer.

Examples of Type 2 hypervisors that run on top of a host operating system are VMware Fusion, Oracle Virtual Box, Solaris Zones and Parallels Desktop.

- **Question:** What terminal settings for terminal emulation software are typically used on a laptop/PC to connect to most Cisco devices?
- **Answer:** Following are terminal settings for terminal emulation software typically used on your laptop/PC to connect to Cisco devices:

  - Speed (baud): 9600

  - Data bits: 8

  - Stop bit: 1

  - Parity: None

  - Flow control: None

Note: These settings are for Cisco devices using IOS and IOS-XE software. For Cisco devices running IOS-XR, the stop bit is set to 2 instead of 1. See Appendix A for a listing of terminal settings for terminal emulation software (such as SecureCRT, PuTTY, xterm or Terminator) used on laptops or PCs to connect to various vendor devices such as Cisco,

Juniper, Alcatel-Lucent, Huawei, Telco and Extreme Networks.

■ **Question:** You are logged into a router (or switch) and while you are typing a command, you get an unsolicited message that interrupts the command you were typing. How can you prevent this from happening?

■ **Answer:** Type the logging synchronous command in the line configuration mode where you are logged in.

Note: In order to prevent being interrupted by unsolicited log messages or debug command outputs (if debug is turned on) while you are typing commands on the device, you must enable logging synchronous on the device. This command synchronizes unsolicited log messages and debug command outputs with your solicited (intended) typing, outputs and prompts through the line (console, VTY, auxiliary) you are currently using so these unsolicited messages do not interrupt your typing of commands or viewing of outputs.

These unsolicited messages, called system log messages (syslog messages), are stored in the log buffer of the device's memory. These messages are extremely helpful when troubleshooting issues with the device. You can view these syslog messages by using the show log command on the device. Syslog messages appear as the following: *sequence number:timestamp: %source-severity-MNEMONIC:description.*

Since these syslog messages can be lost from memory when the device is rebooted, you can send these syslog messages to a syslog server for permanent storage. To send syslog messages to a syslog server, use the logging *<syslog server hostname | syslog server IP address>* command in the global configuration mode of the device.

You can also select which syslog messages you want logged—on the device's memory or on a syslog server—based on the message's severity level. To select what syslog messages you want logged, use the **logging trap** *<severity number>* command in the global configuration mode. When you select a severity number with this command, the device will log all syslog messages at that severity level and higher (the lower the number the higher the severity). In other words, if you used the **logging trap 4** command, the device would log all syslog messages with severity levels of 0 to 4. Following are the 8 severity levels (0–7) of syslog messages:

- **Level 0:** Emergencies—system unstable (example: system shutting down due to overheating)

- **Level 1:** Alerts—immediate action needed (example: system temperature exceeded limit)

- **Level 2:** Critical—critical conditions (example: system nearing temperature limit)

- **Level 3:** Errors—error conditions (example: incorrect configuration)

- **Level 4:** Warnings—warning conditions (example: configuration file written to server via SNMP request)

- **Level 5:** Notifications—normal but significant condition (example: interface status messages)

- **Level 6:** Informational—information messages only (example: access list or port violation)

- **Level 7:** Debugging—debug messages (example: outputs after using the **debug** command)
- ■ **Question:** What version of SNMP provides encryption?
- ■ **Answer:** SNMP version 3 (SNMPv3).

- **Question:** Can you use **ping** to troubleshoot SNMP issues?
- **Answer:** No, the **ping** command can only check for connectivity between the SNMP server and the device; it cannot help you troubleshoot SNMP problems between the server and the device.

Note: Simple Network Management Protocol (SNMP) is used for network monitoring and network device management across UDP ports 161 and 162 (for SNMP traps). Some signs that Simple Network Management Protocol (SNMP) is not working for a device is SNMP process CPU utilization is 70 percent or higher; SNMP services no longer respond; and you receive SNMP error messages.

The **ping** command is a good first step in ensuring there are no connectivity or congestion issues between the SNMP server and the device. However, a **ping** test can prove good while SNMP is still not working. Other things can cause SNMP problems that an ICMP ping cannot detect are firewall rules/NAT or access lists blocking SNMP messages (161 or 162); or SNMP configuration errors on the device or SNMP server such as missing or wrong community string, SNMP user privileges, SNMP version, IP address or Object Identifier (OID).

There are several tools you can download, such as SnmpWalk, SnmpGet and Wireshark, or are part of a monitoring and management system that can check for SNMP problems.

- **Question:** What is the global command used for on Cisco devices?
- **Answer:** A global command is used to configure a Cisco device such as a router or switch. In global configuration mode, a configuration is completed on the running configuration file and it immediately affects the entire device.

Note: All configurations completed in the running configuration must be saved to the startup configuration file in NVRAM or they will be lost during loss of power or reboot of the device.

- **Question:** What are the 3 phases of the Cisco network design life-cycle?
- **Answer:** Plan, Build and Manage. These 3 phases replace the following older 6 phases of the Cisco network design life-cycle:

  - **Prepare (Plan):** Customer and stakeholder inputs about the organization's requirements, goals and limitations are identified. A network strategy is developed to meet those requirements. This strategy will be used to justify the equipment and expenses needed to meet the organization's requirements.

  - **Plan (Plan):** This phase audits the existing network and available resources to gather as much information as possible to accomplish the network strategy that will meet the organizations requirements. A plan is developed based on the responsibilities, scope, cost and resources needed to accomplish the network strategy.

  - **Design (Plan):** This phase is the development of a comprehensive, detailed design that meets the organization's technical and business requirements. The design includes a variety of detailed information and documentation such as rooms, areas, applications and resources affected by the network strategy plan; network and connectivity drawings; rack and cable databases; power, heating, ventilation and air conditioning (HVAC) requirements; equipment identified for change/removal/ upgrade and new equipment to be installed; configuration changes; and pre- and post-implementation network performance checks. All plans and designs are reviewed and approved by all stakeholders before moving to the implementation phase.

- **Implement (Build):** In this phase, the network plan and design is implemented and deployed in the network. Coordination with all stakeholders is communicated before and after implementation. The operational network is handed over to the implementation team. A pre-implementation check of the network is performed and documented as a baseline. This is followed by the implementation and deployment of the planned design. Afterward a post-implementation check of the network is performed to ensure the network is operating as planned and designed.

- **Operate (Manage):** Once the planned design is successfully deployed, the implementation team hands over the operational network back to operations personnel for normal day-to-day network operations. This phase includes the daily managing, monitoring and troubleshooting of the network to ensure it continues to operate as planned and designed.

- **Optimize (Manage):** This phase focuses on optimizing the existing network through continuous and proactive management, monitoring, assessing and tweaking of the network to ensure it is running at an optimized level.

- **Question:** What is the DISA document used for guidance on Tech Control procedures?
- **Answer:** DISA Circular 310-70-1 Defense Information Infrastructure (DII) Technical Control.

Note: You might be asked this question when interviewing for a US government IT job, particularly in the Department of Defense (DoD). DISA is the Defense Information Systems Agency, a DoD organization that provides worldwide DoD WAN backbone connectivity to the DoD and other US government organizations.

■ **Question:** What is the DISA document used for guidance on status reporting?
■ **Answer:** DISA Circular 310-55-1 Status Reporting For Defense Information Infrastructure (DII).

Note: You might be asked this question when interviewing for a US government IT job, particularly in the Department of Defense (DoD).

■ **Question:** What is unified communications?
■ **Answer:** Unified communications, also called converged networks, is an IP-based communications system that combines separate networks—such as a voice network, video network and data network—into one unified network that uses the same communication infrastructure and path for voice, video and data.

Note: This question is about unified communications within the overall network, not the specific Unified Communications (UC) Proxy feature of the Cisco Adaptive Security Appliance (ASA). The question about the ASA Unified Communications will be asked in the Firewall Question and Answer section of volume 5.

Unified communications reduce costs in the following ways:

•   **Moves, adds, changes and roaming profiles:** Personnel moves within an organization, or simply roaming to use another desk, cubicle or office within an organization requires changes to the phone, video and data devices at desks and cubicles. The costs for these moves are reduced when using one unified network versus three separate networks for voice, video and data.

- **Reduced cabling:** The telephone network, video network and data network can use the same cabling infrastructure, reducing costs, maintenance and space requirements.

- **Remote work:** One network line over the Internet can be used for remote voice, video and data networking for personnel working away from their main office.

- **IT staff consolidation for voice, video and data networks:** One unified network can help reduce associated costs for both maintenance and operation requirements for one network versus three separate networks.

- **Application consolidation:** Application features, registration fees, deployment and upgrades on one unified network reduces cost compared to utilizing applications for three separate networks.

MULTICAST ROUTING Q&A

- **Question:** What is multicast?
- **Answer:** Multicast technology uses Protocol Independent Multicast (PIM)-enabled routers throughout the network to replicate and distribute packets of streaming information to destination users rather than requiring the source of the information to transmit multiple copies of the same information to each and every end user.

Note: IP multicast is a way to help reduce congestion and preserve bandwidth on the network when using bandwidth intensive applications such as video conferencing, news, sports and financial streaming as well as a myriad of other voice, video and data streaming services that must be delivered simultaneously to thousands of corporate recipients, homes and mobile users. With multicast, the source of the voice, video or data stream need only send a single copy while the other PIM-enabled routers replicate that single copy for downstream users.

The reason it's called protocol independent is because PIM uses the routing information supplied by existing network routing protocols, such as BGP, OSPF or EIGRP, to discover topologies. Multicast does not have its own topology discovery mechanism. Instead, it uses the mechanisms of these routing protocols existing on the network.

Multicast uses the concept of groups to identify the PIM-enabled router recipients on the network that want the source's information for their respective hosts. This allows the source to transmit packet streams only to the multicast group address, called a rendezvous point (RP), instead of to individual destination hosts. Source Active (SA) messages are used to advertise active sources of information within a multicast domain.

The destination multicast group IP address for each group of information ranges from 224.0.0.0 to 239.255.255.255, with a few exceptions such as the 224.0.0.0 to 224.0.0.255 range that is reserved for the local network segment and 224.0.1.1 used for Network Time Protocol (NTP). The auto-RP group addresses are 224.0.1.39 and 224.0.1.40.

The source of the information still maintains its original unicast IP address throughout the multicast process. Any host device connected to any public network, such as the Internet, can join a particular multicast group by using the Internet Group Management Protocol (IGMP) to connect to the data stream they are interested in receiving.

- **Question:** What is PIM?
- **Answer:** Protocol Independent Multicast (PIM) is the protocol that multicast uses to leverage whatever routing protocol (such as BGP, EIGRP, OSPF or static routes) that exists on the network to forward multicast packets.

Note: PIM is not a routing protocol; it does not perform routing updates;

and it is independent of any IP routing protocol. Therefore, it uses the unicast IP routing table of the routing protocol that currently exists on the network to perform reverse path forwarding (RPF) checks before forwarding multicast packets.

■ **Question:** Where does the traffic from a multicast source get replicated in multicast?
■ **Answer:** Only where the multicast network tree branches out throughout the network.

Note: There are two tree structures in multicast: a source tree, also referred to as a shortest path tree (SPT); and a shared tree. Multicast traffic is replicated only where the SPT tree or shared tree branches out throughout the network as shown in Figure 1-5.

Figure 1-5 *Traffic replication in a multicast tree network*

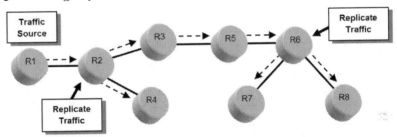

A **source tree (shortest path tree or SPT)** is where every source of multicast traffic is a root that sends out multicast traffic down through the multicast tree to every receiving host who requests that multicast traffic. SPT uses an "S,G" (pronounced "S comma G") where S is the unicast source address and G is the multicast group address.

A **shared tree** uses a single common source as the root, called a rendezvous point (RP), for multiple sources of multicast traffic.

■ **Question:** What is a rendezvous point?

- **Answer:** A rendezvous point is a PIM-enabled router in a multicast network that is a central meeting place (rendezvous) where sources of information can send multicast traffic and where receiving hosts can request this multicast traffic.

Note: A **shared tree** uses a single common source as the root, called a rendezvous point (RP), for multiple sources of multicast traffic as shown in Figure 1-6. PC1 is the source of the multicast traffic. R1 is the first hop router for PC1; therefore, R1 sends this multicast traffic to the RP router. PC2 and PC3 want this multicast traffic. Router R5 is first hop router for PC2 and PC3 that are requesting the multicast traffic; therefore, R5 requests this multicast traffic from the RP router on behalf of PC2 and PC3.

Figure 1-6 *Rendezvous point (RP) in a multicast shared tree network*

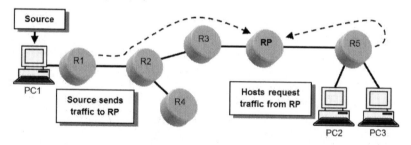

This RP router is where sources of multicast send their traffic; and the RP is where hosts go to when they want that multicast traffic. A shared tree only sends the multicast traffic to the RP; and users only go to the RP instead of requiring a path to every source (as in an SPT tree). All multicast sources and receivers must register (through the router closest to them) with the RP router.

Shared trees using an RP require less CPU and memory in multicast routers and less network bandwidth because they don't have to send multicast traffic to every user requesting that traffic as in an SPT tree.

Shared trees use a "*,G" (pronounced "star comma G") where * is multiple unicast source addresses and G is the multicast group address.

- ■ **Question:** What is Auto-RP?
- ■ **Answer:** Auto-RP dynamically assigns rendezvous point (RP) routers to non-RP routers in a PIM domain instead of you having to manually configure each non-RP router to know which RP router to use for each multicast group address. Auto-RP dynamically maps a set of multicast group addresses (representing multicast traffic) to the same RP router; and distributes these group-to-RP mapping information to all PIM-enabled routers in the multicast domain to ensure all PIM routers in the domain are using the same RP for a set of multicast group addresses.

Note: In vendor routers supporting multicast, auto-RP uses what's called a candidate RP and mapping agent. The candidate RP is a router that is configured to announce that it wants to be an RP for that multicast domain. The candidate RP uses the 224.0.1.39 multicast address to send RP announcement packets out its PIM-enabled interfaces to other routers within the PIM domain to announce its desire to become an RP. By configuring two or more PIM-enabled routers with the 224.0.1.39 address, each of these routers have a chance to announce themselves as a candidate RP.

The mapping agent is a router in the PIM domain that is configured to listen to the RP announcements from candidate RPs; makes a list of these possible RPs; automatically selects which of these candidate RPs will become the RP for that PIM domain; and then uses the 224.0.1.40 multicast discovery group address to send a discovery message out all of its PIM-enabled interfaces by dense mode flooding to all the other routers within the multicast domain to notify them of the RP router that was selected. This is how all routers in the multicast domain automatically discover which RP to use to receive multicast group traffic. When two or more routers announce themselves as candidate RPs for the same multicast group or set of groups, the mapping agent selects the candidate RP router with the highest IP address as the RP. Therefore it is best to use loopback interfaces with IP addresses for your RP addresses. This way, the RP address is never withdrawn when a physical interface goes down on the RP router; and you can control which router will become the RP for a multicast group depending on the higher IP address you configure on the loopback address.

If for some reason, the RP router fails, the mapping agent will automatically select another RP among the configured candidate RPs; and sends another 224.0.1.40 discovery message to all PIM-enabled routers in the multicast domain to notify them of the new RP.

It is also possible to configure one router to be both an RP candidate and the mapping agent or you can configure multiple routers to be RP candidates and mapping agents. You can have multiple RPs within a multicast domain; however, only one RP is selected per multicast group traffic. Either one RP can be configured to handle all multicast groups or several RPs can be used, each RP configured to handle different multicast groups. Access lists are typically used to separate multicast groups among two or more RPs being used within a PIM domain.

Auto-RP information takes precedence over static RP information.

- **Question:** What are the two standard auto-RP group addresses for announcing and discovering the RP?
- **Answer:** 224.0.1.39 and 224.0.1.40.

- **Question:** What is Dense Mode?
- **Answer:** PIM-Dense Mode (PIM-DM) uses a flood and prune method for distributing multicast traffic from source to receivers. This push model floods multicast throughout the network regardless of whether or not the multicast receivers requested this traffic. Any downstream PIM-enabled routers that do not have host receivers that need this multicast stream will automatically prune this unwanted traffic.

Note: PIM-Dense Mode (PIM-DM) is advantageous in networks where every subnet in the network are active multicast receivers. PIM-DM only supports multicast Source Trees (SPT) and does not use a rendezvous point. This downstream flooding and pruning of multicast traffic occurs every 3 minutes in PIM-DM. Dense Mode does not scale well to large networks because it requires many branches in the multicast Source Trees.

- **Question:** What is Sparse Mode?
- **Answer:** PIM Sparse Mode (PIM-SM) uses a pull model for distributing multicast traffic from source to receivers. PIM-SM will only send multicast traffic to registered active multicast receivers requesting the multicast group traffic. PIM-SM uses a rendezvous point (RP) router as the central point for sending and requesting the multicast traffic.

Note: PIM-SM only supports multicast Shared Trees. PIM-SM allows multicast traffic to remain fixed on the Shared Tree or to be re-routed through other PIM-enabled routers closer to the original source that have joined the Shared Tree. This provides a more optimized direct path from source to destination on the distribution tree. PIM-SM scales well to large networks because it requires fewer branches than PIM-DM in the distribution tree from multicast sources to receivers.

- **Question:** What is Sparse-Dense Mode?
- **Answer:** Sparse-Dense-Mode (PIM-SM-DM) will initially flood multicast group traffic throughout the network (PIM-DM push model) until it detects a rendezvous point (RP) for a particular group. It will then treat that multicast group and its respective RP with the PIM-SM pull model and only send that multicast group traffic when requested by host receivers.

Note: PIM-SM-DM uses both push and pull models for distributing multicast traffic from the multicast source to receivers. PIM-SM-DM supports both Source Trees and Shared Trees. Sparse-Dense Mode can operate with or without a rendezvous point. If it does not detect an RP on the network, it will use dense mode. When it detects an RP, it will operate in sparse mode.

- **Question:** How do you configure dense mode multicast?
- **Answer:** Following are the two required commands to configure dense-mode multicast:

  - In the global configuration mode, enable multicast on the router by configuring the ip multicast-routing command. This required command must be configured on all routers in the multicast topology within the domain.

  - In the interface configuration mode, enable Protocol Independent Multicast dense mode (PIM-DM) on the interface by using the ip pim dense-mode command. All interfaces participating in multicast on this router must be configured with this command.

- **Question:** How do you configure sparse mode multicast?
- **Answer:** Following are the required commands to configure sparse-mode multicast:

  - In the global configuration mode, enable multicast on the router by configuring the ip multicast-routing command. This required command must be configured on all routers in the multicast topology within the domain.
  - In the interface configuration mode, enable Protocol Independent Multicast sparse mode (PIM-SM) on the interface by using the ip pim sparse-mode command. All interfaces

participating in multicast on this router must be configured with this command.

- Configure the Rendezvous Point (RP) on the selected router within the domain. The RP must be configured for either sparse mode (PIM-SM) or sparse-dense mode (PIM-SM-DM).

Note: More than one multicast-enabled router can be configured as the RP. Two of the most common RPs to configure are the static RP and the auto-RP. Following are the required commands for configuring either of these two types of RPs.

Configuring Static RP

In the global configuration mode configure the following required command on the router selected as the rendezvous point.

Router1(config)#**ip pim rp-address** *<IP address of RP>* *[ACL]* **[override] [bidir]**

Note: The optional access list (ACL) uses a standard IP ACL, with number range from 1 to 99, to identify the IP addresses of multicast groups allowed by the RP. By default, auto-RP would be used when there is a conflict between the two types of RPs—static RP and auto-RP. However, the optional **override** keyword can be used to ensure the configured static RP is chosen instead of the auto-RP during a conflict. The optional **bidir** keyword is used when you are configuring a Bidirectional PIM (bidir-PIM).

Configuring Auto-RP

In the global configuration mode configure the following required commands for auto-RP.

Router1(config)#**ip pim autorp listener**

Note: The **ip pim autorp listener** command is used only with sparse mode (PIM-SM) on all PIM-enabled routers. Do not use this command with sparse-dense-mode (PIM-SM-DM). This command ensures the auto-RP group addresses 224.0.1.39 and 224.0.1.40 are PIM dense mode flooded out all interfaces configured with PIM-SM.

Router1(config)#**ip pim send-rp-announce** *<interface | IP address>* **scope** *<TTL>* [group-list *<ACL>*] [interval *<seconds>*] [bidir]

Note: This command enables the PIM-enabled router to announce itself as a candidate RP. The *<interface | IP address>* argument in this command identifies the RP either by an interface or IP address. The **scope** keyword defines the maximum hops allowed in time-to-live (TTL) value. The optional **group-list** keyword uses a standard IP ACL, with number range from 1 to 99, to identify the IP addresses of multicast groups allowed by the RP. The optional **interval** keyword defines the interval in seconds that auto-RP announcement messages are sent. The optional **bidir** keyword is used when you are configuring a Bidirectional PIM (bidir-PIM).

Router1(config)#**ip pim send-rp-discovery** [*interface*] **scope** *<TTL>* [interval *<seconds>*]

Note: This command configures this PIM-enabled router as the RP mapping agent, and is only configured on an RP router. An RP router must be identified as the RP mapping agent to identify all RP candidates in the multicast domain through RP announcement messages; automatically selects the RPs among the RP candidates; maps RPs to multicast group traffic; and then dense-mode floods these group-to-RP mappings to all other multicast-enabled routers in the PIM domain. The optional **interface** argument identifies the IP address used as the source address for the mapping agent. The **scope** keyword defines the maximum hops allowed in time-to-live (TTL) value for auto-RP discovery messages. The optional **interval** keyword defines the interval in seconds that auto-RP discovery messages are sent—the default value is 60 seconds.

- **Question:** How do you configure sparse-dense mode multicast?
- **Answer:** Following are the required commands to configure sparse-dense mode multicast:

  - In the global configuration mode, enable multicast on the router by configuring the **ip multicast-routing** command. This required command must be configured on all routers in the multicast topology.

  - In the interface configuration mode, enable the interface with Protocol Independent Multicast sparse-dense mode (PIM-SM-DM) using the **ip pim sparse-dense-mode** command. All interfaces participating in multicast on this router must be configured with this command.

  - Configure the rendezvous point on the selected router within the PIM domain or configure auto-RP that will select the RP for you. An RP must be configured whenever using sparse mode (PIM-SM) or sparse-dense mode (PIM-SM-DM).

- **Question:** How do rendezvous points in one domain learn about and use multicast sources in another domain?
- **Answer:** Rendezvous points in one domain will communicate with RPs in another domain through the Multicast Source Discovery

Protocol (MSDP) to learn about and use multicast sources in each of their domains.

Note: RPs in the separate domains will use MSDP to establish a TCP peering session on port 639 with border routers or RPs of other domains to learn about external multicast sources. Then these RPs (or border routers or possibly a combination of both) will forward the multicast traffic to each other to provide this traffic to receivers in their own domain. This can be done between multiple MSDP peers of different service providers throughout the Internet; and gives service providers the autonomy to have their own RPs while learning about and receiving multicast traffic from the RPs of other service provider networks.

- **Question:** What is Reverse Path Forwarding in multicast?
- **Answer:** Reverse Path Forwarding (RPF) is the forwarding process multicast uses to prevent routing loops while forwarding multicast traffic away from the source to destination receivers. A multicast-enabled router does this by using the router's existing unicast routing table to first check the interface where it initially received the multicast source traffic (called an RPF check). It then uses that RPF check as a baseline for filtering out and dropping the same multicast traffic if it receives it on another interface.

Note: As long as the multicast-enabled router receives the multicast traffic on the correct interface where it initially received that traffic, it will forward it through its PIM distribution tree branches to downstream receivers that requested that traffic. If the multicast traffic arrives on the wrong interface, it will be considered a loop and will be dropped.

- **Question:** What protocol do hosts use to request multicast traffic?
- **Same Question:** How do hosts request multicast traffic?
- **Same Question:** How do hosts join a multicast group?

■ **Answer:** Hosts use the Internet Group Management Protocol (IGMP) to request multicast traffic from a local multicast router.

Note: Internet Group Management Protocol (IGMP) is the protocol used between hosts and their local first hop multicast router for joining and leaving multicast groups. Hosts that request a particular data stream will dynamically be registered for the correct multicast group by the local first hop IGMP-enabled router providing that information. The local PIM router will also use the IGMP messages from their hosts to request new multicast groups from sources or trim multicast groups no longer used by hosts. Figure 1-7 shows an example of how multicast group traffic is requested by host receivers.

Figure 1-7 *Multicast group traffic*

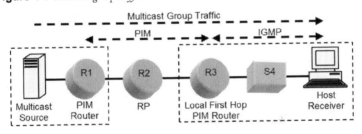

There are three versions of IGMP:

- **IGMP Version 1 (IGMPv1)** contains the following:

  - **Membership Report:** Hosts will send this message to the local first hop PIM-enabled router to indicate they wish to join a particular multicast group.

  - **Membership Query:** The local PIM-enabled router will send this IGMP message to hosts on its subnets to determine if a particular group stream is still needed by hosts. If at least one host responds before the end of three consecutive query attempts, the router will continue providing that multicast group feed. If no host responds, the router will stop forwarding that group traffic, freeing up network bandwidth.

- IGMPv1 is also known as Any-Source Multicast (ASM).

- **IGMP Version 2 (IGMPv2)** contains the following:

    - **Version 1 Membership Report:** Works the same as in **IGMPv1**.

    - **Version 2 Membership Report:** Works the same as in **IGMPv1**.

    - **Membership Query:** Works the same as in **IGMPv1**.

    - **Leave Group:** Unlike **IGMPv1**, this version 2 allows hosts to send a message to the local first hop PIM-enabled router stating they are done with their request for a particular group feed. This will prompt the local PIM router to issue a query to see if any hosts want this group stream, and if there are no responses, the local PIM router will end the group feed, freeing up network bandwidth much quicker than version 1.

    - IGMPv2 is also known as Any-Source Multicast (ASM).

- **IGMP Version 3 (IGMPv3)** is a Source Specific Multicast (SSM) that contains the following:

    - **Source Filtering:** Hosts will send this message to the local first hop PIM router to indicate which multicast groups they want and specific sources from which they want to receive the multicast traffic. It uses an INCLUDE mode to identify the specific sources from which to receive multicast traffic; and an

EXCLUDE mode to identify the specific sources from which it does not want to receive multicast traffic.

- **Membership Query:** Works the same as in **IGMPv1**.

- Does not use a rendezvous point (RP).

- IGMPv3 is used in source-specific multicast (SSM).

IGMP is used for IPv4 networks only. For multicast in IPv6 networks, Multicast Listener Discovery (MLD) and ICMPv6 is used. MLD version 1 (MLDv1) for IPv6 performs similar functions as IGMPv2; and MLDv2 has similar features as IGMPv3.

- ■ **Question:** What is multicast ASM?
- ■ **Answer:** Any-Source Multicast (ASM) is the traditional multicast (IGMPv1 or IGMPv2) that uses any multicast source address with a multicast group (*,G) address; and uses a rendezvous point (RP) with either sparse-mode or sparse-dense-mode.

Note: RFC 1112 defines traditional IPv4 multicast, known as Any-Source Multicast (ASM), addresses as falling within the multicast range of 224.0.0.0 through 239.255.255.255. ASM uses Internet Group Multicast Protocol version 2 (IGMPv2).

- ■ **Question:** What is multicast SSM?
- ■ **Answer:** Source-specific multicast (SSM) uses IGMP version 3 (IGMPv3). It uses an INCLUDE mode to identify the specific sources from which hosts can receive multicast traffic; and an EXCLUDE mode to identify the specific sources from which hosts do not want to receive multicast traffic. SSM does not use a rendezvous point (RP).

Note: Source-specific multicast (SSM) uses IGMP version 3 (IGMPv3). It is a multicast extension that uses multicast source and group (S,G) addresses; and does not use a rendezvous point (RP). It allows multiple multicast sources (S) to send traffic to the same multicast group (G) number, but only to receivers (hosts) that join (request) the source-specific address and multicast group address combination.

In 2006, RFC 4607 defined SSM IPv4 addresses as falling within the multicast range of 232.0.0.0 to 232.255.255.255 (232.0.0.0/8) and the prefix address FF3x::/32 for SSM in IPv6.
SSM uses IGMPv3 instead of IGMPv1 or IGMPv2 as in Any-Source Multicast (ASM).

In traditional multicast or ASM (IGMPv1 or IGMPv2), multicast groups are identified with the *,G (pronounced "star comma G") to represent a multicast source address and a multicast group address. An SSM group, called a channel, is identified with the S,G. The S represents the source-specific address and the G represents the SSM group. This means ASM identifies a set of multicast hosts by the multicast group (G) address only, whereas SSM identifies a set of multicast hosts by both the multicast source (S) and group (G) addresses.

An ASM multicast group address can be used by only one source address. Since SSM identifies the multicast group address by both a source and group address, multiple multicast source (S) addresses can be used with the same multicast group (G) address.

Since SSM does not require rendezvous points, you do not need auto-RP or Bootstrap Router (BSR) when configuring SSM.

With SSM, receiving hosts have greater flexibility in requesting multicast source traffic. Additionally, by explicitly requesting specific multicast source traffic, hosts have the added protection against denial of service (DoS) attacks. ASM is more susceptible to DoS attacks because receivers do not differentiate the sources (*) where they receive multicast group

(G) traffic.

Configuring SSM requires you to still enable multicast routing with the **ip multicast-routing** command in the global configuration mode; the **ip pim sparse-mode** command on each multicast enabled interface; in addition to using the **ip pim ssm** command in the global configuration mode and the **ip igmp version 3** command in the interface configuration mode as shown in the following commands.

Router(config)#**ip multicast-routing** (use on all PIM-enabled routers)
Router(config)#**ip pim ssm <default | range <*ACL*>>** (the **default** keyword uses the 232/8 address range or you can specify your SSM address range with an ACL)

Router(config-if)#**ip pim sparse-mode** (use on all multicast-enabled interfaces)
Router(config-if)#**ip igmp version 3** (use on all host-facing interfaces)

To view multicast group information, use the **show ip igmp groups** or **show ip mroute** commands.

- **Question:** What is the strict mode and loose mode used for in multicast?
- **Answer:** The strict and loose modes are used for the Reverse Path Forwarding (RPF) check. In **strict mode**, all packets from the source must always be received on the interface the multicast router uses to reach the source; otherwise, the packet is dropped. Strick mode is typically used with IGMPv1 and IGMPv2 in Any-Source Multicast (ASM).

  In **loose mode**, the source address of the packet only has to match the longest prefix in the routing table of that multicast router. This allows the packet to be received from different interfaces without being discarded during the RFP check. Loose mode is typically used in IGMPv3 Source-Specific Multicast (SSM).

- **Question:** What is Anycast RP in multicast?
- **Answer:** Anycast RP is used when two or more RPs are used within a single multicast sparse mode (PIM-SM) domain for fault tolerance and load sharing for multicast traffic. Anycast RP uses the same RP loopback IP address with a /32 bitmask on all the RP routers in the same domain.

Note: Anycast RP uses MSDP between peering RPs in the same sparse mode (PIM-SM) domain in similar fashion to RPs in different PIM-SM domains that use MSDP. The multiple RPs in the same multicast domain will use MSDP to share multicast source information for the same group addresses.

Anycast RP is enabled by configuring the same RP loopback IP address with a /32 bitmask on all the RP routers in the same domain. The RP's loopback address is configured on downstream PIM-enabled routers as the RP to go to for multicast group traffic. Downstream routers wanting multicast traffic will then register with the closest RP with that IP address. The existing routing protocol (BGP, OSPF, EIGRP, etc.) on the network will automatically choose the closest RP to route multicast traffic to active receivers—this provides load balancing. When one of the RPs fails, the routing protocol in use will converge based on its metrics and automatically select another RP in the same domain to provide multicast traffic to the active receivers of the failed RP—this provides fault tolerance.

SECTION TWO

Transmission Lines and Cabling Q&A

DATA RATES Q&A

- **Question:** How much bandwidth is a DSO?
- **Answer:** 64 Kbps which is traditionally one voice or data channel.

- **Question:** How much bandwidth is a T1?
- **Answer:** 1.544 Mbps that traditionally provides 24 voice or data channels.

- **Question:** How much overhead is in a T1?
- **Answer:** Alternate Mark Inversion (AMI) line code uses 192Kbps of overhead per T1 which gives you 1.352Mbps for actual traffic.

Note: AMI line code uses up 8Kbps of overhead per 64 Kbps channel, leaving you 1.352 Mbps for the T1 data (1.544Mbps – 192Kbps = 1.352Mbps).

With Bipolar 8 with Zero Substitution (B8ZS) line code, there is no overhead—you have the full T1 (1.544 Mbps) for actual traffic.

- **Question:** How many T1's are in a DS3?
- **Answer:** There are 28 T1's in a DS3.

- **Question:** What is the data rate of OC-3?
- **Answer:** 155.5 Mbps.

- **Question:** What is the data rate of OC-12?
- **Answer:** 622 Mbps.

- **Question:** What is the data rate of OC-24?
- **Answer:** 1.2 Gbps.

- **Question:** What is the data rate of OC-48?
- **Answer:** 2.5 Gbps.

- **Question:** What is the data rate of OC-192?
- **Answer:** 9.6 Gbps.

TDM Q&A

- **Question:** What is TDM?
- **Answer:** Time Division Multiplexing (TDM), was a commonly used multiplexing technique in communication systems. It samples each voice, video or data channel successively from channel 1 to 24 of a T1. It then converts the sampled voice, video or data signals to digital signals, and each of these sampled channels of bits are placed in individual time slots one after the other. After 24 channels are sampled once, TDM will repeat this sampling process again until each of the 24 channels are sampled a total of 8 times—this is referred to as Nyquist's theory. When all 24 channels are sampled 8 times as described, one synchronization bit is added to these samples. The result is a 193 bit frame (24 x 8 = 192 + 1 = 193) for one T1. These 193-bit frames are sent to the receiving end where each of the 8 samples from each frame are extracted and reassembled into voice, video or data signals across 24 channels.

Note: A Superframe is 12 of these sampled T1 frames, and an Extended Superframe (ESF) is 24 of these sampled T1 frames.

When earlier technology reached the point where we now wanted to convert analog signals such as voice signals to digital signals, many people presented a sampling theorem to accomplish this. In 1920, Americans Harry Nyquist and Claude Shannon presented a sampling theory that is now known as the Nyquist-Shannon sampling theorem or simply the Nyquist theory.

Their theorem stated that if you sample voice frequencies (200Hz–4KHz) at twice its highest frequent (8KHz since the highest voice frequency is approximately 4KHz), you would have enough samplings of the human voice to represent it in digital format of 1's and 0's. You would then be able to transmit these digital 1's and 0's to a receiver that could convert that digital representation back to a voice frequency that is intelligible to the human ear.

CABLING AND PINOUTS Q&A

- **Question:** How far can you run RS530 cable before having to use a repeater?
- **Answer:** 350 feet for data rates up to 1024 Kbps. 1700 feet for data rates up to 256 Kbps. 4000 feet for data rates up to 64 Kbps.

- **Question:** What is the maximum distance of Cat5e, Cat6 and Cat6a cabling?
- **Answer:** Cat5e and Cat6 both have a maximum cable length of 100 meters (328 feet) for 10/100/1000 Mbps speeds. Cat6a provides a maximum cable length of 100 meters (328 feet) for 10Gbps traffic, while Cat6 provides a maximum cable length of 55 meters (180 feet) for 10Gbps traffic.

Note: Cat5e does not support 10Gbps traffic. Cat6a is able to provide greater cable length—100 meters (328 feet)—compared to 55 meters (180 feet) maximum cable length for Cat6 due to the higher frequency (500Mhz) of Cat6a.

Cat6 supports higher speeds (250 Mhz) with less crosstalk that Cat5e (100Mhz). Cat6 has less crosstalk than Cat5e due to pairs of wires in Cat6 being insulated—something Cat5e does not have.

Cat6a supports higher speeds (500Mhz) than both Cat5e (100Mhz) and Cat6 (250Mhz). Cat6a has less crosstalk than Cat6 because Cat6a is considerably thicker than Cat6 due to thicker insulation around each individual wire and tighter winding of each pair of wires.

- **Question:** What is the difference between Cat5 and Cat6 cabling?
- **Answer:** Cat6 has lower crosstalk, less noise and less loss than Cat5.

Note: Cat6 has lower crosstalk, less noise and less loss than Cat5 (54db versus 43db, respectively, of nearend crosstalk at 100Mhz). This translates to Cat6 having a better signal-to-noise ratio than Cat5. In other words, Cat6 is 12 times less noisy than Cat5.

The better signal-to-noise ratio of Cat6 is due in part to more twists per inch of each pair of wires in Cat6 over Cat5. This better signal-to-noise ratio at higher bandwidth of Cat6 over Cat5 (250Mhz versus 100Mhz, respectively) makes Cat6 more reliable (fewer errors) for current applications and able to handle higher data rates for future applications. Cat6 is backward compatible with Cat5 and Cat3.

- **Question:** How many wires (pins) are in Ethernet cable connector?
- **Answer:** 8 wires (pins).

- **Question:** What is the name of the pinout standard commonly used in Ethernet cable connectors—T568A or T568B?
- **Answer:** T568B.

Note: Figure 2-1 shows the cable pinouts for a straight-through Ethernet cable in the T568B standard. For more information about T568A or T568B Ethernet cable connector pinouts, see Appendix H.

Figure 2-1 *Straight-through Ethernet cable pinouts for RJ-45 connectors for T568B cabling (10Base-T, 100Base-TX, and 1000Base-T)*

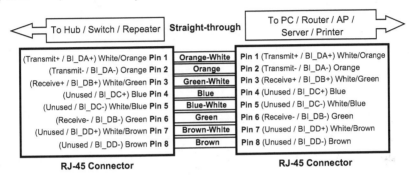

- **Question:** What pinouts are crossed on both ends of an Ethernet crossover cable (10Base-T and 100Base-TX)?
- **Answer:** Pin 1 connects to pin 3. Pin 2 connects to pin 6.

Note: Other than crossover pins 1, 2, 3 and 6, the other pins are straight-through (pins 4, 5, 7 and 8 on one connector connects to pins 4, 5, 7 and 8, respectively, on the other connector end of the Ethernet cable. For more information about T568A or T568B Ethernet cable connector pinouts, see Appendix H.

- **Question:** You want to connect a router to another router. What type of Ethernet cable should you use?
- **Answer:** A crossover cable.

Note: For more information about straight-through and crossover cable connections between network devices, see Appendix H.

- **Question:** You want to connect a router to switch. What type of Ethernet cable should you use?

- **Answer:** A straight-through cable.

- **Question:** What are the pinouts at both ends of a console (rollover) cable?
- **Answer:** Pin 1 to pin 8; pin 2 to pin 7; pin 3 to pin 6; and pin 4 to pin 5.

- **Question:** Can you connect 50 micron fiber cable to 62.5 micron fiber cable?
- **Answer:** Although you can connect both 50 micron and 62.5 micron fiber cables to devices such as switches, routers or servers, it is not advisable to connect 50 micron fiber directly to 62.5 micron fiber because this will create an excessive loss of power when light of the larger diameter 62.5 micron fiber tries to fit in the smaller diameter core of the 50 micron fiber cable.

Note: This may seem like an obvious and ridiculous question, but it was actually asked in an IT job interview. Although 50 micron fiber has a smaller core than 62.5 micron fiber, 50 micron multimode fiber provides three times more bandwidth than 62.5 micron fiber (500Mhz-km at up to 550m versus 160Mhz-km at up to 220m, respectively). Thus, 50/125 fiber can be used as a fiber backbone inter- or intra-building connection for higher bandwidth needs (10Gbps) over longer distances than 62.5-micron.

Multimode fiber typically uses 50 and 62.5 micron fiber that can span 1804.5 feet (roughly 6 football fields). Singlemode uses 9 micron fiber cable that also handles bandwidth up to 10Gbps and is typically used for very long distances (long-haul) up to 6.2 miles (10km).

- **Question:** What are the three primary wavelengths used in fiber cables?
- **Answer:** 850 nanometers (nm), 1300 nm and 1550 nm.

Note: Fiber cables can use either light emitting diodes (LEDs) or laser light sources. There are three primary wavelengths of light for fiber optics: 850, 1300 and 1550 nanometers (nm). These three wavelengths are chosen because the attenuation produced by the absorption and scattering effects within fiber cable is much less at those wavelengths. The US National Institute of Standards and Technology (NIST) uses these three wavelengths in their power meter calibrations for fiber optics. Therefore, manufacturers use these same wavelengths in their design and test of fiber optics.

LED light that typically uses 850 or 1300 nm produces a lower power source than laser light that typically uses 1310 or 1550 nm. 850 nm LEDs were prevalent in devices in the 1980s and 1990s. Therefore, the larger diameter 62.5 micron fiber was originally deployed in commercial and government network infrastructures during those years instead of the smaller diameter 50-micron fiber. The 850 nm LEDs provided a greater power budget when used with the larger 62.5 micron diameter than it did with the 50 micron diameter.

Multimode cable can use either 850 or 1300 nm. Laser light typically uses 1300 nm for multimode fiber.

Singlemode fiber uses either 1310 or 1550 nm; therefore, laser light typically uses either 1310 or 1550 nm for singlemode fiber.

- **Question:** What are the maximum distances for singlemode fiber cable?
- **Answer:** The maximum distance for singlemode is 10 kilometers (6.2 miles).

Note: Data rates in fiber cabling is inversely proportional to distance. In other words, the higher the data rate in fiber, the shorter the distance data can travel through fiber cabling.

- **Question:** What are the maximum distances for multimode fiber cable?
- **Answer:** The maximum distance for multimode is 550 meters (1804.5 feet)—about the length of 6 football fields.

- **Question:** How thick is singlemode fiber cable?
- **Answer:** Singlemode fiber is 9 micron thick in diameter.

- **Question:** How thick is multimode fiber cable?
- **Answer:** Multimode fiber is either 50 micron or 62.5 micron thick in diameter.

Note: Multimode fiber has a larger core diameter (50 or 62.5 micron) than the 9 micron core of singlemode fiber, allowing multiple wavelengths of light to pass through multimode fiber versus only a single wavelength of light that can pass through the 9 micron singlemode.

Today, 62.5/125-micron multimode fiber (125 represents the diameter of the cladding surrounding the 62.5 micron fiber core) is still commonly used in many fiber network infrastructures such as at the desktop and for adding segments to your existing network.

As bandwidth, speed and distance requirements continue to increase, more organizations are leaning toward using 50 micron multimode fiber to fill their backbone requirements. Although 50 micron fiber has a smaller core than 62.5 micron fiber, 50 micron multimode fiber provides three times more bandwidth than 62.5 micron fiber—500Mhz-km at up to 550m (1804.5 feet) versus 160Mhz-km at up to 220m (721.8 feet), respectively.

Thus, 50/125 fiber can be used as a fiber backbone at inter-building or intra-building connections for higher bandwidth speeds (10Gbps) over longer distances than 62.5 micron can support.

The singlemode 9 micron fiber cable also handles bandwidth up to 10Gbps and is typically used for very long distances (long-haul) up to 10km (6.2 miles).

Either duplex or simplex fiber strands can be used with multimode or singlemode fiber cables. Duplex fiber cable contains a pair of fiber strands that allow simultaneous bi-directional data transfer for devices such as fiber switches and servers, fiber modems and workstations. Simplex fiber cable contains single fiber strands for either transmitting data or receiving data one-way. However, Dense Wavelength Division Multiplexing (DWDM) now makes it possible to combine and transmit multiple signals simultaneously at different wavelengths on the same single strand of fiber cable.

SECTION THREE

Voice over IP (VoIP) Q&A

ADVANTAGES AND DISADVANTAGES OF VoIP Q&A

- **Question:** What is IP telephony?
- **Answer:** IP telephony is the name given to technology that transmits voice communications over an IP-based network.

- **Question:** What are some advantages of using VoIP?
- **Answer:** Following are some advantages of using VoIP:

  - Low cost due to one converged network carrying voice, video and data across one network or one service provider. Less equipment, cabling, infrastructure, operation and maintenance costs required for VoIP versus using traditional PSTN phones on its own separate phone network.

  - Greater portability and flexibility of VoIP calls versus traditional PSTN phone calls.

  - More advanced features on a VoIP phone versus traditional PSTN phone, such as improved video-conferencing and collaboration.

- **Question:** What are some disadvantages of using VoIP?
- **Answer:** Following are some disadvantages of using VoIP:

  - VoIP is more sensitive to latency (delay), packet loss and jitter than other applications.

- Reliability and quality is based on the local network and Internet connections that can affect the latency, jitter and packet loss of VoIP traffic.

Note: The biggest disadvantage of VoIP is the requirements for the quality of calls. VoIP call monitoring, also referred to as quality monitoring (QM), is used to test, monitor, analyze and troubleshoot call quality issues across a VoIP network.

- Latency restrictions of VoIP traffic leading to increased QoS requirements.

- Additional bandwidth required on a converged (data, video and voice) network or device.

- VoIP phones require a power source, such as a wall outlet or PoE power from another device. When your power goes out, the VoIP phone goes out. Traditional Public Switched Telephone Network (PSTN) phones receive power through the PSTN network that receives its power from the PSTN central station. If you are using a PSTN network when your power goes out, your PSTN phone could still be working.

- VoIP traffic is susceptible to hacking, viruses and worms just as other data on the network.

- Difficulty in locating the caller of emergency 911 calls because VoIP phones use IP addresses that are unrelated to the caller's physical location. This makes it difficult for emergency calls to be directed to an emergency call center nearest the caller. Phone numbers of the traditional PSTN phone system are directed to the nearest emergency call center based on the phone number of the caller.

PROTOCOLS USED WITH VoIP Q&A

- **Question:** What transport protocol is used in VoIP for the actual stream of data carrying voice content?
- **Answer:** VoIP uses connectionless UDP packets to carry voice data.

- **Question:** What transport protocol is used in VoIP for the signaling that controls the conversation?
- **Answer:** Either UDP or TCP.

Note: "Call signaling" or "signaling" is the term used to describe the setup and teardown of the signal. In other words, call signaling sets up and tears down the voice call. It is not the protocol that is used for the actual voice communication; it simply sets it up and tears it down.

- **Question:** What are some protocols used in VoIP?
- **Answer:** Following are some protocols used in VoIP:

  - **H.323:** Developed by the International Telecommunications Union (ITU) as a call signaling protocol for voice, video conferencing and data across packet-switched (IP) networks. H.323 and Session Initiation Protocol (SIP) are the two most commonly used VoIP protocols.

  - **Session Initiation Protocol (SIP):** A call signaling protocol developed by 3Com as an alternative to H.323. SIP is an Internet Engineering Task Force (IETF) standard protocol for call signaling of VoIP and multimedia communication sessions. SIP is supported by IETF and is not compatible with H.323 which is supported by ITU.

  - **MEGACO (H.248):** A call signaling protocol developed by Cisco as an alternative to H.323.

- **Skinny Client Control Protocol (SCCP):** A Cisco proprietary IP-based call signaling protocol that allows skinny clients (such as a Cisco VoIP phone or computer) to communicate with H.323 systems. SCCP is used with the Cisco Unified Communications Manager (CUCM) for call signaling. SCCP is oftentimes referred to simply as Skinny. The term "skinny" is used to mean SCCP is a lightweight (simple and uncomplicated) protocol.

- **Media Gateway Control Protocol (MGCP):** An open standard call signaling protocol developed by Cisco that is used to control Gateways remotely from different vendor Media Gateway Controllers or call agents, such as a Cisco CUCM, AVAYA IP EPABX or Nortel CS1000E. MGCP allows Media Gateway Controllers (call agents) to know and control the state of each port on Gateways. Whereas SIP and H.323 are considered peer-to-peer protocols, MGCP is a server-client protocol supported by IETF.

- **Jingle XMPP VoIP extensions:** A call signaling protocol developed by Google and the Extensible Messaging and Presence Protocol (XMPP) Standards Foundation. Jingle is an extension to XMPP that provides signaling for voice, video and multimedia. XMPP is the de facto standard for instant messaging and presence (telepresence or collaboration) in peer-to-peer (P2P) communications. Jingle uses RTP to transport the real-time voice, video and multimedia traffic.

- **Real-time Transport Protocol (RTP):** A protocol used within UDP packets to transport real-time streaming voice, video and multimedia traffic across a packet-switched (IP) network. RTP was developed by IETF and is considered the primary standard for real-time streaming of audio, video and multimedia traffic across packet-switched (IP) networks. RTP is not used for call signaling.

- **Real-time Transport Control Protocol (RTCP):** A protocol used along with RTP within UDP packets to monitor the transport and quality of real-time streaming voice, video and multimedia traffic across a packet-switched (IP) network.

- **Secure Real-time Transport Protocol (SRTP):** A protocol developed by Cisco and Ericsson that provides encryption, message authentication and integrity, and replay protection for RTP data (real-time streaming voice, video and multimedia traffic).

- **Inter-Asterisk eXchange (IAX):** This protocol gets its name from Asterisk, an open source communications project sponsored by Digium. IAX is a protocol used to transport VoIP sessions and streaming video between servers and terminal devices across packet-switched (IP) networks. Unlike other protocols that use separate protocols for signaling and payload, IAX uses the same UDP packet to transport both the signaling protocol and the real-time voice, video or multimedia traffic, typically across UDP port 4569. This protocol simplifies configuration of firewalls and other packet inspection devices and network address translators. IAX was replaced by IAX2 defined in RFC 5456.

- **Skype protocol:** A closed-source protocol developed by Microsoft via Skype Technologies (Microsoft acquired Skype in 2011) for peer-to-peer voice and video communications across the Skype IP telephony network. Skype is powered entirely by Microsoft-operated supernodes.

- **Session Description Protocol (SDP):** The protocol used to negotiate which media types and formats of the streaming voice, video or multimedia will be used between two or more endpoints. This protocol is typically contained in the body part of SIP. SDP includes session announcement, session invitation and parameter negotiation that the source of the information advertises to destination users so they have the parameter information to join in the session with their endpoint equipment.

H.323 AND SIP Q&A

- **Question:** What is H.323?
- **Answer:** H.323 is the International Telecommunication Union-Telecommunication Standardization Sector (ITU-T) recommendation that defines the protocols (such as call signaling and control for call setup, maintenance and teardown, multimedia transport and control, and bandwidth control for point-to-point and multi-point conferences) to support VoIP and multimedia communication sessions on a packet-switched (IP) network.

Note: H.323 is the most commonly used VoIP call signaling protocol. First published by the ITU in 1996, H.323 is considered older than Session Initiation Protocol (SIP) that was standardized by IETF in 1999 by RFC 2543. Both H.323 and SIP are two commonly used signaling protocols for voice and video conferencing systems over IP networks.

H.323 is a binary code-based protocol that runs on the layer 4 TCP or UDP transport protocol. H.323 can be used in a mixture of IP, public switched telephone network (PSTN), Integrated Services Digital Network (ISDN) and Q-Signaling (QSIG) over ISDN networks. H.323 understands IP addresses or hostnames, and supports the Uniform Resource Identifier (URI)-style addressing used in the SIP protocol.

Telepresence devices that use H.323 include endpoints such as terminals (user devices such as an IP phone, tablet or videoconferencing system to participate in a conference call), Multipoint Control Units (MCUs) and Gateways and codecs, in addition to non-endpoint devices such as Gatekeepers, Border Elements and Peer Elements.

A **codec** is a device that encodes and decodes data streams or signals. It encodes during signal transmission and decodes during signal reception or playback. Commonly used codec devices for VoIP are G.711 and G.729.

Gateways allow H.323 networks, such as VoIP, to communicate with other networks, such as PSTN or ISDN networks, or with other voice and videoconferencing protocols such as SIP, H.320 or H.324.

Gatekeepers provide optional features to a telepresence system such as endpoint registration, address resolution, admission control and user authentication.

Border Elements are signaling devices that are located on the edge of a single administrative domain and communicate with Border Elements in other domains in the end-to-end telepresence network. Border Elements can also communicate with Peer Elements and Gatekeepers within their own domain. **Peer Elements** are located within a single domain and help to propagate telepresence traffic within their own domain—not outside their administrative domain. Following are addresses and aliases that H.323 supports:

- Generic H.323 ID

- E.164 dialed digits

- Uniform Resource Identifier (URI)

- Uniform Resource Locator (URL)

- Integrated Services Digital Network (ISDN) User Part (ISUP) number

- Transport address

- Email address

- Party number

- Mobile User Identity Module (UIM)

- **Question:** What are the three minimum addresses that must be configured on an endpoint device that is using H.323 if these addresses are not provided by a DHCP server?
- **Answer:** (1) The endpoint device (such as an IP phone) IPv4 address with appropriate netmask; (2) the default gateway for the endpoint; and (3) the IPv4 address of the centralized controller or call agent, such as a Cisco Unified Communications Manager (CUCM).

- **Question:** What is SIP?
- **Answer:** The Session Initiation Protocol (SIP) is an Internet Engineering Task Force (IETF) standard protocol for call signaling of VoIP and multimedia communication sessions. All the other parts of the session (such as call control, multimedia transport and control, and bandwidth control for point-to-point and multi-point conferences) to support the VoIP or multimedia communications on a packet-switched (IP) network are performed by other protocols.

Note: SIP was designed by Mark Handley, Henning Schulzrinne, Eve Schooler and Jonathan Rosenberg in 1996 and was standardized in 1999 by RFC 2543. SIP is a text-based protocol (similar to HTTP and SMTP text) layer 6 (application layer) protocol that is independent of the underlying TCP, UDP and Stream Control Transmission Protocol (SCTP) layer 4 (transport layer) protocol.

SIP only understands Uniform Resource Identifier (URI)-style addressing, not IP addresses or hostnames used in the H.323 protocol. A URI is a string of characters used to identify a name of a web resource. Two types of URI that you are perhaps more familiar with are the Uniform Resource Locator (URL) that uses the http or https scheme and Uniform Resource Name (URN) that uses the urn scheme. RFC 2396 defines the URI syntax which takes the form of *scheme:[//[user:password@]host[:port]][/]path[?query][#fragment]*.

SIP and H.323 are two commonly used signaling protocols for voice and multimedia conferencing systems over IP networks. SIP takes an Internet-oriented approach (IETF) to set up and tear down multimedia communication sessions over IP, providing a client-to-server architecture that uses a centralized controller or call agent, such as a Cisco Unified Communications Manager (CUCM), to route calls.

H.323, on the other hand, takes a more telecommunications-oriented approach (ITU) to set up and tear down voice and video over IP, providing a peer-to-peer architecture that supports user-to-user (or terminal-to-terminal) communications without the use of a centralized controller agent such as a CUCM.

Since the SIP text-based protocol is less defined and a more open protocol than the H.323 binary code-based protocol, every vendor can— and has in many cases—developed their own version of SIP with unique vendor-specific extensions. This can create interoperability problems between different vendor equipment using their own version of SIP.

The SIP signaling protocol is not compatible with the H.323 signaling protocol. In order to get SIP devices to communicate with H.323 devices, a gateway device is used to translate messages between the two different protocols.

DEVICES USED IN VoIP Q&A

■ **Question:** What are some of the devices used in a VoIP network?
■ **Answer:** Typical devices used in a VoIP network are Terminals, Gateways, Gatekeepers and Multipoint Control Units (MCUs).

Note: Since VoIP uses many of the same devices used in video over IP and collaboration (presence) networks, you'll find both VoIP and video over IP sharing similar devices and protocols. Here is a breakdown of each of these devices used in VoIP:

- **Terminal:** Endpoint devices such as VoIP phones or desktop computers.

- **Gateway:** A Gateways is an interface that translates formats between the packet-switched (IP) network and the circuit-switched network (PSTN). This allows digital IP packets of the new generation IP phone (VoIP) system to interconnect with the Time Division Multiplexing (TDM) or Pulse Code Modulation (PCM) telephony traffic of an old generation PSTN phone system.

  Gateways perform call setup and teardown, codec functions for converting analog audio (voice) or video to digital IP packets, and compression/decompression of digital signals for transmission.

  Gateways fall into one of two basic categories: analog gateways or digital gateways.

  An analog VoIP gateway can function as either a FXS gateway or an FXO gateway. An FXS gateway is used to connect your traditional analog phone and fax machines to a VoIP phone system. An FXO gateway is used to connect your VoIP phone system to a PSTN phone system.

A digital VoIP gateway can also function in two ways. It is used to connect a VoIP phone system to either a digital system, such as a T1, E1 or BRI digital line; or it can be used to connect a traditional PBX phone system to a packet-switched (IP) network.

There are a multitude of different types of vendor Gateways, and they can be a standalone device or can be a voice module within a router. VoIP gateways can support multiple voice codecs, such as GSM, iLBC, G.711, G.722, G.726, G.728 and G.729.

Since VoIP protocols determine how your voice packet is transported across the network, you must ensure your Gateway is using the correct signaling protocol (such as H.323, SIP, H.248, SCCP or MGCP), the correct transport protocol (such as RTP or IAX) along with other protocols that may be used, such as RTCP (monitoring), SRTP (encryption) and SDP (negotiation of media types and formats). Gateways communicate with Gatekeepers, using the Registration, Admission and Status (RAS) protocol, to coordinate VoIP calls.

- **Gatekeeper:** An H.323 device used for call control and management for groups of H.323 devices known as zones. Typically, a single zone is controlled by a single Gatekeeper; however, there can be more than one Gatekeeper per zone for load balancing or backup. Each Gatekeeper provides address translation, admission control, bandwidth management and control, and call authorization and management for the zone it is controlling. Gatekeepers can be a software application or integrated into terminals (endpoint devices) or Gateways.

- **Multipoint Control Unit (MCU):** Used to coordinate, manage and control communications between three or more terminals (endpoint devices) or Gateways so they can participate in a single multipoint conference session. An MCU can be a standalone device or integrated into Gateways, Gatekeepers or terminals (endpoint devices).

Figure 3-1 shows one of many ways these VoIP devices can be deployed in a VoIP network.

Figure 3-1 *Devices used in a VoIP network*

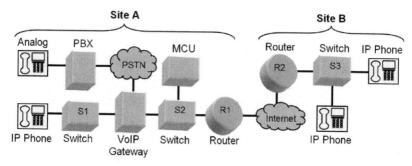

- **Question:** What is a softswitch?
- **Answer:** A softswitch is used to provide call control for establishing, maintaining, routing and terminating VoIP call sessions.

Note: It's called softswitch because it is an industry-standard VoIP software-based solution that runs on different vendor hardware devices. It is used to bridge a VoIP network with a public switched telephone network (PSTN); as well as aid in transitioning from PSTN to VoIP.

MULTIPOINT CONTROL UNIT (MCU) Q&A

- **Question:** What is a Multipoint Control Unit (MCU)?
- **Answer:** An Multipoint Control Unit (MCU) is an endpoint device used in VoIP, voice conferencing and videoconferencing to connect,

manage and control multiple endpoint devices or gateways so they can participate in a single VoIP or video conference session.

Note: The MCU is referred to as a bridging system, conference bridge or MCU server. The MCU allows you to scale to a large number of endpoint devices in a single voice conference or video conference session. When you dial into a conference session, most likely your conference call is being handled by the MCU. The MCU consists of a Multipoint Controller (MC controller) and Multipoint Processors (MP processors).

The MC controller handles the coordination of different multimedia parameters between endpoints such as codec (G.711, G.722, G.729, etc.), call signaling protocols (SIP or H.323), frame rate and resolution as shown in Figure 3-2.

The MP processor handles the processing, mixing and switching of multimedia traffic.

The MCU also provides options to endpoint users such as split screen, picture-in-picture and voice-activated speakers. The MCU can be deployed as either a hardware device (hardware bridge) or virtualized software (software bridge) on another device such as a server.

You can access the MCU through either the MCU web GUI or the MCU console port.

Figure 3-2 *MCU used to connect multiple endpoints for multi-conference sessions*

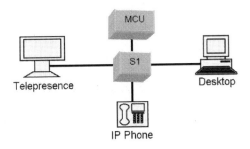

CODEC Q&A

- **Question:** What is a codec device used for?
- **Answer:** The codec (encoder-decoder) device converts analog audio/video signals into compressed digital signals for transmission across an IP network. The codec device at the other end will decompress the digital signals and convert the digital back to analog audio/video signals for the user on the other end.

Note: The codec device originated from the Nyquist theory in the early 1900's. When technology reached the point where it was now possible to convert analog signals, such as voice signals, to digital signals (a process called quantization), many people presented a sampling theorem to accomplish this conversion. Among these people were two Americans, electronic engineer Harry Nyquist (in 1928 when he wrote about this study) and mathematician, electrical engineer and cryptographer Claude Shannon (in 1948 when he proved Nyquist's sampling theorem). Their theory is now known as the Nyquist-Shannon sampling theorem or simply the Nyquist theory.

Their theory stated that if you sample voice frequencies (200Hz – 4KHz) at twice its highest frequent (8KHz—since the highest voice frequency is 4KHz), you would have enough samplings of the human voice to represent it in digital format of 1's and 0's. You could then transmit the digital signals to a receiver that could convert that digital representation back to a voice frequency that is intelligible to the human ear.

Over time, Nyquist's sampling rate has been incorporated into other advances in communications technology. For example, the Data Service 0 (DS0), which is 64,000 bits per second (64Kbps), is the basic data rate in telecommunications from which all other data rates are described. 64Kbps is a multiple of Nyquist's 8KHz theorem (8,000 x 8 = 64,000); and each data rate, such as T1, DS3, OC3, OC193, 10Gbps and 100Gbps are all multiples of 8,000.

Nyquist's theorem translated over to the world of IP data bits. Each bit of data uses multiples of the number 8. For example, in IT networks each byte of data is made up of 8 bits in IPv4, and each octet in IPv4 addressing is 8 bits long.

Today, codecs are commonly used for Voice over IP (VoIP). Codec devices such as the G.711, an ITU-T codec standard, samples audio at a rate of 64,000 times per second (64Kbps) to convert these samples to uncompressed digital signals for high quality voice transmission. Other codecs will compress the digital signal, such as the G.722 codec that can sample audio at three different rates: 48Kbps, 56Kbps and 64Kbps. G.726 uses a 32Kbps sampling rate. G.729 uses an 8Kbps sampling rate. Uncompressed digital signals require more bandwidth than compressed.

CISCO UNIFIED COMMUNICATIONS MANAGER (CUCM) Q&A

■ **Question:** What is the Cisco Unified Communications Manager (CUCM)?

■ **Answer:** The CUCM is a call-routing device providing centralized command and control to configure, setup, manage, teardown and monitor voice and video communications in a converged network.

Note: The Cisco Unified Communications Manager (CUCM), formally called the Cisco Call Manager, is also referred to as Cisco UCM, Unified CM or UCM. The CUCM operating system is based on Red Hat Linux. You can access the CUCM either through a Web GUI or CLI commands.

CUCM uses either SIP or SCCP—not H.323—to communicate with Cisco IP phones for call setup, teardown and additional service features requested by the IP phones, such as call forwarding or conferencing. However, the CUCM can interoperate with H.323 phones via a Gateway. Once the IP call is setup, CUCM is no longer involved with the call between the IP phones. The phones use the Real-Time Transport

Protocol (RTP) to transport and communicate audio and video between callers.

The CUCM can be deployed as a hardware, software or virtual solution in the form of the public cloud, private cloud, on-premises, remote or hybrid. Other features on the CUCM include a host-based intrusion prevention system (HIPS) and a DHCP server to provide IP addresses to IP telephony (VoIP) devices.

GATEKEEPER AND GATEWAY Q&A

- **Question:** What is a Gatekeeper used for in VoIP?
- **Answer:** A Gatekeeper is a device that performs zone management, address translation, admission control, bandwidth control and user authentication for a VoIP system.

- **Question:** What is a Gateway used for in VoIP?
- **Answer:** A Gateway is a device that allows different vendor voice and video conferencing devices with different standards or protocols to communicate with each other across a VoIP or telepresence system.

Note: A Gateway is an interface that translates different formats between the packet-switched (IP) network and the circuit-switched (PSTN) network. This allows digital IP packets of the newer generation IP phone (VoIP) system to interconnect with the Time Division Multiplexing (TDM) or Pulse Code Modulation (PCM) telephony traffic of an older generation PSTN phone system. Gateways also perform call setup and teardown, codec functions for converting analog audio (voice) or video to digital IP packets, and compression/decompression of digital signals for transmission.

CONFIGURE A SWITCH FOR VoIP AND DATA Q&A

- **Question:** How do you configure a switch port for voice and data?
- **Answer:** The configuration below shows the required commands in the interface configuration mode to allow a switch port to pass both data and voice traffic.

```
Switch(config-if)#switchport mode access
Switch(config-if)#switchport access vlan 10
Switch(config-if)#switchport voice vlan 20
```

Note: Figure 3-3 helps to visualize the answer above. VLAN10 will allow data traffic from PC1. VLAN20 will allow voice traffic from the IP phone. When using both data and voice across the same switch port, you typically connect the IP phone to the access port on the switch, and then connect the PC to a port on the IP phone.

Figure 3-3 *A switch port configured to allow data and voice traffic*

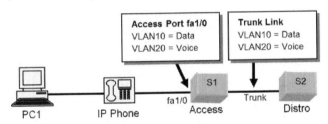

Referring to Figure 3-3, the IP phone will send voice traffic to the switch S1 as tagged (VLAN) 20 traffic. The PC1 will send data traffic to the IP phone as untagged (no VLAN number) traffic which the IP phone will pass on to switch S1 as untagged traffic. Since port Fa1/0 on switch S1 is configured in access mode and placed in VLAN 10, the untagged traffic from PC1 will automatically be placed in VLAN 10.

Cisco Discovery Protocol (CDP) must be enabled on the switch in order for the switch to identify the Cisco IP phone; inform the Cisco IP phone what voice VLAN to use; and place voice traffic from the IP phone in the configured voice VLAN on the switch.

However, CDP is a Cisco proprietary discovery protocol that can only be used with Cisco products, including Cisco IP phones. If you are using a non-Cisco IP phone with a Cisco switch, the non-Cisco IP phone will not understand CDP. Therefore, you must hardcode the voice VLAN number on the non-Cisco IP phone so that non-Cisco IP phone will use the correct VLAN number when sending voice traffic to the Cisco switch. The same holds true if you use a Cisco IP phone with a non-Cisco switch.

If the switch port is a Power over Ethernet (PoE) port, this port can provide power to the IP phone. However, the PC connected to the IP phone would still require 110VAC power from a wall outlet.

Voice traffic is highly sensitive to delay; therefore, voice traffic needs to be given higher priority over other traffic on the network. QoS markings are used to give voice traffic higher precedence over other traffic. Cisco IP phones automatically mark their voice traffic with a higher Class of Service (CoS) priority.

When you have a Cisco IP phone connected to a Cisco switch, you can use the **mls qos trust device cisco-phone** or **auto qos voip cisco-phone** or **auto qos voip cisco-softphone** commands in the interface configuration mode of the switch, and that switch's port will automatically trust the QoS marking of voice traffic from the Cisco IP phone. The **auto qos** keywords cause the Cisco switch or router to automatically apply some QoS settings that are considered best practices for the IP phone.

When you have a non-Cisco IP phone connected to a Cisco switch, you can use the **mls qos trust cos** or **auto qos voip trust** commands in the interface configuration mode of the switch, and that switch's port will automatically trust the QoS marking of voice traffic from the non-Cisco IP phone.

TROUBLESHOOTING VoIP QUALITY Q&A

- **Question:** A customer complains that their VoIP calls are experiencing crackling or skipping of the voice in the call? How would you troubleshoot this?
- **Answer:** Use the Media Gateway Controller (call agent)—such as a Cisco Unified Communications Manager (CUCM), AVAYA IP EPABX or Nortel CS1000E—to access the VoIP Gateway to see if there are any drops (discards) in buffer packets on the interface for that voice call having problems. If there are, this is an indication of jitter on that voice call. To resolve this jitter issue, increase the range on the adaptive mode of the jitter buffer to dynamically adjust to the amount of jitter present on the network.

Note: Type the **show voice call summary** command on the Gateway to see the identity and states of each voice call on each interface on the Gateway.

- **Question:** Problems with VoIP quality usually falls into one of six areas. Can you name some of these areas?
- **Answer:** Latency, packet loss, jitter, Internet connection, device issues (such as a router CPU issue) or improper configurations.

- **Question:** How much latency is acceptable in a VoIP call?
- **Answer:** Latency up to about 150ms end-to-end is an acceptable VoIP call.

Note: Latency is the amount of time it takes a packet of information (voice, video or data) to travel **one-way** from its source to its destination or **roundtrip** from source to destination and back to the source again. Another term for latency is delay because latency is oftentimes measured in terms of the delay time (in milliseconds or ms) of packets to reach a destination. Voice and video traffic are more sensitive to network delays (latency) and packet loss than other network applications.

Low latency means there is small delay in packets traversing a network; and high latency means there is large delay in packets reaching their destination through the network. Each VoIP packet is transmitted every

20ms. Latency up to 150ms end-to-end is an acceptable VoIP call. Latency above 150ms end-to-end impacts the quality of the call; and latency of 300ms is an unacceptable VoIP call leading to customer complaints; however, this is can be managed through IP accelerators.

- **Question:** What kinds of problems can latency cause to a VoIP call?
- **Answer:** Latency in VoIP calls can cause the following problems:

- Delays in the two-way communication of voice packets between two people on the phone, resulting in overlapping noises where the voices of both parties on each end are interrupting each other.

- Echo

- Synchronization problems between voice, data or video packets such as during video conferences.

Note: Some areas to look at to troubleshoot latency issues are congestion on the network either locally or on the service provider's network; adequate bandwidth for VoIP, data and video requirements on the converged network; chokepoints or bottlenecks such as firewalls of other inspection devices slowing down or blocking packets; hardware such as codecs devices, routers or switches; software issues such as configurations or applications such as anti-viruses.

Ping tests and traceroutes are used to check latency across networks because they provide millisecond readings of the travel time of packets.

- **Question:** What types of delay are common in VoIP calls?
- **Answer:** Propagation delay, handling delay and queuing delay.
  Note: Here are the differences between propagation delay, handling delay and queuing delay:

- **Propagation delay:** This delay is found in the media path the VoIP packets take from source to destination. This path could include a mixture of fiber and copper cabling, satellite shots or line-of-site radio communications. Much of the delay in these types of paths are inherent in the properties and systems used.

- **Handling delay:** This delay is found in the devices that handle, process, inspect and redirect voice packets. Oftentimes, this delay is inherent in the device capabilities themselves. Other times, misconfigurations can increase delays and other processing issues to voice packets. Improperly configured quality of service (QoS) configurations on devices end-to-end can cause latency issues.

- **Queuing delay:** This delay is due to outbound interfaces or jitter buffers holding onto voice packets in a queue before transmitting them to their destination or after receiving them from the source. The more traffic going through an interface, the more delay may be imposed on some packets in the queue.

■ **Question:** What are some things that can cause packet loss in VoIP calls?

■ **Answer:** Many of the issues that cause delay of voice packets can also cause loss of voice packets, such as network congestion, misrouted packets, buffer overflows, inherent propagation delays and misconfigurations can cause loss of voice, video and other packets.

Note: Applications that use TCP as its layer 4 transport protocol can recover from packet loss through retransmission. However, voice and video packets use UDP as its transport protocol and; therefore, are more sensitive to packet loss than other network applications causing degradation in voice quality.

Packet loss can vary from crackling or skipping (dropping in and out) of the voice in the call to complete degradation in voice quality based on the amount of packet loss.

Ping tests can reveal packet loss as well as delay on VoIP networks. Checking error counts on interfaces of devices, such as routers, switches and gateways, can also show when packets are dropping.

- **Question:** What is jitter?
- **Answer:** Jitter, also referred to as packet delay variation (PDV), is the variation or change in the time (delay or latency) it takes for a packet to travel from source to destination.

Note: If it takes 60ms one-way every time for a packet to travel from a source IP phone to a destination IP phone, then the VoIP network is experiencing no jitter. However, if it takes 60ms one time for a packet, 80ms the next time, and then 70ms another time, then the VoIP network is experiencing jitter (variations or changes) in the time it takes for packets to travel one-way from source to destination.

These variations or shifts (jitter) among packets traveling from source to destination are usually unnoticed when it comes to viewing a webpage or reading text or data on your computer screen or mobile devices. However, these variations are easily noticed in real-time voice and video communications. For video, jitter may cause your picture to freeze or skip for an instant. For voice, jitter can cause crackling or skipping (dropping in and out) of the voice in the call.

Jitter of real-time voice and video streaming can be caused by network congestion, device processing delays, timing drift, route changes, improper queuing or configuration errors. The source of the jitter problem can be on the local network or within the service provider's network.

A solution for jitter is to use a jitter buffer (also referred to as de-jitter buffer or playout delay buffer) at the receiving end of the VoIP connection that temporarily stores arriving packets to help minimize delay variations to provide evenly spaced intervals of arriving packets to the IP phone.

There are two types of jitter buffers: static and dynamic. A static jitter buffer is hardware-based configured by the vendor of the VoIP device. Static jitter buffers may be configured for 30ms to 50ms in depth. A dynamic jitter buffer is software-based that you can configure to run in adaptive mode to dynamically adapt and adjust to jitter issues occurring in the network. Dynamic jitter buffers might be set to 100ms–200ms.

To troubleshoot jitter using Cisco devices, perform these steps:

- Telnet to the VoIP Gateway that is involved in the call having jitter problems. Make sure you enable Terminal Monitor to see console messages during the telnet or SSH session.

Note: Gateways can be accessed remotely from different vendor Media Gateway Controllers or call agents, such as a Cisco CUCM, AVAYA IP EPABX or Nortel CS1000E.

- Type the **show voice call summary** command on the Gateway. This command will show you the identity and states of each voice call on each interface on the Gateway.

- In the call summary, locate the interface of the voice call that is suspected of experiencing jitter.

- Issue the **show voice call** *<interface>* command using the interface of the voice call with possible jitter issues.

- In the interface output of the **show voice call** *<interface>* command, check the section under "DSP VOICE VP_ERROR STATISTICS". This section is similar to error count section in a **show interface** command on a Cisco router or switch. Look at the number of "Buff Overflow Discard(ms)" that are shown. This counts the number of packets that are dropped due to being outside of the range of the playout delay buffer (jitter buffer). If "Buff Overflow Discard(ms)" shows continued drops when you repeat the **show voice call** *<interface>* command, this is a direct indication of excessive jitter.

- To help counter these jitter problems, you can readjust the range on the adaptive mode of the jitter buffer to dynamically adjust to the amount of jitter present on the network. This doesn't isolate the cause of the jitter problem—you may still have to troubleshoot that; but this will help prevent the jitter from affecting the voice call through that interface on the Gateway.

  Jitter buffers add latency (delay) to received voice packets being transmitted from source IP phone to destination IP phone by virtue of the buffer holding onto the packet. The more you increase the depth of jitter buffer size, the more delay you can add to each voice packet. (Remember: latency over 150ms end-to-end is an unacceptable VoIP call.) Therefore, care must be taken on how deep you adjust the range of the adaptive mode of the jitter buffer.

- **Question:** You are responsible for a VoIP system within an enterprise. How do you troubleshoot a jitter problem across a service provider network?
- **Answer:** The service provider would have to troubleshoot the Internet connection to ensure the jitter problem is not originating from the SP network.

Note: If you are working for a local network enterprise, your Internet connection will be provided by a service provider (SP). Service providers oftentimes limit the amount of ping tests and traceroutes you can see through their network for security reasons. You may only be able to troubleshoot sources of jitter problems within your own network domain; not external networks such as the SP network. Therefore, the service provider would have to troubleshoot the Internet connection to ensure the jitter problem is not originating from the SP network.

You do have a say in the matter though by ensuring your service provider is providing your network the necessary quality of service (QoS) for your voice and video packets based on the service level contract to ensure your voice and video receive higher quality than other types of traffic.

- **Question:** You are troubleshooting your VoIP system within your enterprise. All devices and configurations look good within your local network. How do you troubleshoot devices and configurations across a service provider network?
- **Answer:** The service provider would have to troubleshoot and ensure the VoIP problem is not originating from the SP network.

Note: As with your Internet connection, you will only be able to troubleshoot VoIP issues among the devices and configurations within your own network domain; not the service provider's domain.

Concerning devices, ensure your own equipment can properly handle voice traffic. This may mean purchasing a VoIP capable router or other devices that can properly handle, control and manage your voice traffic.

Improper configurations are human error issues and; therefore, they can be controlled and managed. Making sure your network personnel are knowledgeable and properly trained to configure VoIP devices will help ensure configurations do not cause VoIP issues. One area you want to ensure is configured correctly is your quality of service (QoS) configurations end-to-end.

- **Question:** What metrics are used to measure VoIP quality?

- **Answer:** Network jitter, delay (latency), packet loss and Mean Opinion Score (MOS).

Note: The Mean Opinion Score (MOS) is a numerical value representing the "perceived" quality of VoIP and multimedia communications from the user's perspective. MOS is a subjective measurement of the overall quality of the IP network used for VoIP that takes into consideration the codec in use, audio-to-digital conversion, compression/decompression and transmission (such as bandwidth, delay and jitter) of the VoIP signal. Many vendor VoIP monitoring tools will show you the MOS reading.

The MOS measurement is defined in ITU-T PESQ P.862 standard. The MOS measurement uses a value range of 1–5, with 1 being the lowest perceived voice quality and 5 being the highest perceived voice quality.

To calculate the perceived voice quality (MOS), an R-Factor score is used that takes into account both user perceptions (User R-Factor) and network equipment impairments (Network R-Factor). Many vendor VoIP monitoring tools will show you the R-Factor reading.

Table 3-1 shows how the R-Factor translates to the MOS value on a per-call basis.

Table 3-1 *Mean Opinion Score (MOS) chart*

Desirability Scale	R-Factor	MOS Value
Desirable	94–80	4.4–4.0
Acceptable	80–70	4.0–3.6
Reach Connection	70–50	3.6–2.6
Not Recommended	50–0	2.6–0

There are several MOS calculations that can be used. Table 3-1 is just one of several rating scales that can be used. Although most ratings typically range from 1–5, there are ranges from 1–100. The following elements are used to calculate the R-Factor:

- **R-Factor** = $Ro - Is - Id - Ie + A$

- **Ro** = Signal to noise ratio

- **Is** = Impairments simultaneous to voice signal transmission

- **Id** = Impairments delayed after voice signal transmission

- **Ie** = Effects of equipment impairment (MOS is converted to Ie)

- **A** = Advantage factor (attempts to account for caller expectations)

■ **Question:** Your manager asks you, "Why should we keep our more expensive MPLS for VoIP phones when we could use the less expensive IPsec VPN for our VoIP phones?" What is your answer?

■ **Answer:** MPLS provides the necessary QoS for delay-sensitive applications such as VoIP, video and other real-time packets. IPsec does not provide QoS to guarantee low latency, packet loss or jitter.

Note: Although an IPsec VPN may provide greater security, bandwidth or speed at a cheaper cost, it does not provide QoS needed to properly treat VoIP or video traffic as higher priority among other types of traffic.

■ **Question:** Fragmentation size on an interface is lower than the VoIP packet size. Is this good or bad and why?

■ **Answer:** This is bad because it will fragment the VoIP packet which should never be fragmented, delayed, dropped or resent as in TCP.

■ **Question:** You have to apply QoS to VoIP packets that are being dropped. What is the recommended QoS classification and marking method, and the recommended queueing mechanism for these VoIP packets with QoS markings?

■ **Answer:** The Modular QoS CLI (MQC) method for QoS marking and low latency queueing (LLQ) mechanism are recommended.

Note: The Modular QoS Command Line Interface (MQC) uses the class-map, policy-map and service-policy commands. The **class map** identifies the VoIP traffic (usually by referencing an ACL); the **policy map** applies QoS action on the VoIP and non-VoIP traffic identified by the class map; and the **service policy** applies the VoIP policy to an interface. Using the MQC method for QoS classifications allows these MQC modules to be used multiple times on multiple interfaces—something not possible with normal CLI commands. In the QoS marking for VoIP using the MQC method below, **ACL 100** identifies the VoIP packets (from UDP ports 16384 to 32767) and H.323 signaling packets (TCP 1720); **class-map** VoIP_Traffic references ACL 100; **policy-map** MQC_for_VoIP sets the QoS markings for VoIP (VoIP_Traffic) and non-VoIP (class-default) traffic; and **service-policy** MQC_for_VoIP applies this MQC module to the inbound interface Ethernet1/0. For more detailed information on QoS, see Volume 6 of *IT Questions & Answers for IT Job Interviews*.

```
Router1(config)#access-list 100 permit udp any any range 16384 32767
Router1(config)#access-list 100 permit tcp any any eq 1720

Router1(config)#class-map VoIP_Traffic
Router1(config-cmap)#match access-group 100

Router1(config)#policy-map MQC_for_VoIP
Router1(config-pmap)#class VoIP_Traffic
Router1(config-pmap-c)#set ip precedence 5
Router1(config-pmap)#class class-default
Router1(config-pmap-c)#set ip precedence 0

Router1(config)#interface Ethernet1/0
Router1(config-if)#service-policy input MQC_for_VoIP
```

SECTION FOUR

Video and Telepresence over IP Q&A

TELEPRESENCE BASICS Q&A

- **Question:** What is video telephony?
- **Answer:** Video telephony is the name given technology that transmits video communications, such as live or recorded video streaming and video conferencing and collaboration, over an IP-based network.

Note: Other names that refer to video telephony are video teleconference (VTC), telepresence, immersive telepresence, presence and video collaboration.

- **Question:** What is telepresence?
- **Answer:** Telepresence is the name given to audio and video technologies that allow individuals and groups in separate locations to participate in the same meeting session in ways that make all participants appear or feel more as if they are all physically present together in the meeting.

Note: The term "telepresence" was first introduced in 1980 by the American cognitive scientist Marvin Minsky in his article that expanded on the existing teleoperation concept to include the idea of making a remote person feel as if they were present in another location.

In 2006, Cisco Systems introduced the term Cisco TelePresence in the name of a line of Cisco products that provide a videoconferencing experience that resemble a single conference room regardless of location. Although telepresence and videoconferencing may seem like the same thing, telepresence conferences seek to provide a more life-like video experience between participants in physically separate locations to make the remote participant appear more present in the room with you—thus the name telepresence. A common example of telepresence is a videoconferencing system where people can meet face-to-face in a one-on-one, one-to-many or many-to-many audio and video setting to communicate or collaborate on any topic.

Telepresence technology also allows you to share video presentations in just about any format during the telepresence discussion. Although Cisco has the greatest worldwide market share of telepresence products, there are many vendors in the telepresence market today such as Apple Polycom, HP, Huawei, Blue Jeans, Avaya, BT Conferencing, ClearOne, LifeSize, Logitech, Radvision, ShoreTel, VidSoft and ZTE.

- **Question:** What is immersive telepresence?
- **Answer:** Immersive telepresence uses very large videoconferencing screens and a seating layout that makes you feel as if the participants on the screen are physically present in the room with you.

Note: Immersive telepresence screens are much larger screens that display remote participants in lifelike size and placed in close proximity to your meeting table to give the appearance that these remote participants are seated across the table from you in the same room.

- **Question:** What are telepresence endpoints?
- **Same Question:** What are video conference endpoints?
- **Answer:** Endpoints are the devices of a video conference or telepresence system that the end user can control. Endpoints include the devices used to make and engage in a video conference call such as a phone, PC, tablet, camera and monitor.

Note: In telepresence or videoconferencing documentation, you will also find the term endpoint being used to identify other local devices that support the telepresence call such as a Cisco Unified Communication Manager (CUCM), Cisco Multipoint Control Unit (MCU) or a codec device. TelePresence endpoints are also referred to as TelePresence collaboration endpoints or simply endpoints.

MULTIPOINT CONTROL UNIT (MCU) Q&A

■ **Question:** What is a Multipoint Control Unit (MCU)?
■ **Answer:** An Multipoint Control Unit (MCU) is an endpoint device used in videoconferencing to connect multiple endpoint devices or gateways so they can participate in a single multipoint conference session; and manages and controls the multipoint conference traffic from the centralized MCU device.

Note: The MCU allows you to scale to a large number of endpoint devices in a single videoconference session. Figure 4-1 shows the MUC connecting multiple endpoints for telepresence sessions.

Figure 4-1 *MCU used to connect multiple endpoints for videoconference sessions*

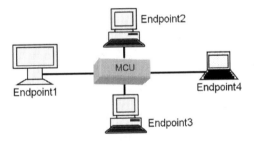

The MCU consists of a Multipoint Controller (MC controller) and Multipoint Processors (MP processors). The MC controller handles the coordination of different multimedia parameters between endpoints such as codec (H.264 or VP8), call signaling protocols (SIP or H.323), frame rate and resolution. The MP processor handles the processing, mixing and switching of multimedia traffic.

The MCU is referred to as a bridging system, conference bridge or MCU server. The MCU also provides options to endpoint users such as split screen, picture-in-picture and voice-activated speakers. The MCU can be deployed as either a hardware device (hardware bridge) or virtualized software (software bridge) on another device such as a server.

The MCU, in addition to the Cisco TelePresence Video Communication Server (VCS), is required for the Cisco TelePresence Multiway feature on endpoints. You can access the MCU through either the MCU web GUI or the MCU console port. The Cisco TelePresence Multipoint Switch (CTMS), which basically performed the same function as the MCU, reached its end-of-life on July 29, 2013 and end-of-sale on January 27, 2014.

GATEKEEPER Q&A

- **Question:** What is a gatekeeper used for in telepresence (videoconferencing)?
- **Answer:** A gatekeeper is a device that performs address translation, admission control, bandwidth control, user authentication and zone management for a telepresence system.

Note: A gateway is a device that allows different vendor videoconferencing devices with different standards or protocols to communicate with each other across a telepresence system. The gateway will perform transcoding between the different vendor endpoints, Multipoint Control Units (MCUs) and other telepresence devices to allow these devices to interwork with each other.

H.323 AND SESSION INITIATION PROTOCOL (SIP) Q&A

- **Question:** What is H.323?

- **Answer:** H.323 is the ITU-T recommendation that defines the protocols to support VoIP, video and multimedia communication sessions on a packet-switched (IP) network.

Note: H.323 is the International Telecommunication Union-Telecommunication Standardization Sector (ITU-T) recommendation that defines the protocols (such as call signaling and control for call setup, maintenance and teardown, multimedia transport and control, and bandwidth control for point-to-point and multi-point conferences) to support VoIP, video and multimedia communication sessions on a packet-switched (IP) network.

First published by the ITU in 1996, H.323 is considered older than Session Initiation Protocol (SIP) that was standardized by IETF in 1999 by RFC 2543. Both H.323 and SIP are two commonly used signaling protocols for voice and video conferencing systems over IP networks. H.323 is the most commonly used VoIP call signaling protocol.

H.323 is a binary code-based protocol that runs on the layer 4 TCP or UDP transport protocol. H.323 can be used in a mixture of IP, public switched telephone network (PSTN), Integrated Services Digital Network (ISDN) and Q-Signaling (QSIG) over ISDN networks. H.323 understands IP addresses or hostnames, and supports the Uniform Resource Identifier (URI)-style addressing used in the SIP protocol.

Telepresence devices that use H.323 include endpoints such as terminals (user devices such as an IP phone, tablet or videoconferencing system to participate in a conference call), Multipoint Control Units (MCUs), Gateways and codecs, in addition to non-endpoint devices such as Gatekeepers, Border Elements and Peer Elements.

A codec is a device that encodes and decodes data streams or signals. It encodes during signal transmission and decodes during signal reception or playback.

Gateways allow H.323 networks to communicate with other networks, such as PSTN or ISDN networks, or with other videoconferencing protocols such as SIP, H.320 or H.324.

Gatekeepers provide optional features to a telepresence system such as endpoint registration, address resolution, admission control and user authentication.

Border Elements are signaling devices that are located on the edge of a single administrative domain and communicate with Border Elements in other domains in the end-to-end telepresence network. Border Elements can also communicate with Peer Elements and Gatekeepers within their own domain.

Peer Elements are located within a single domain and help to propagate telepresence traffic within their own domain; not outside their administrative domain.

Following are addresses and aliases that H.323 supports:

- Generic H.323 ID

- E.164 dialed digits

- Uniform Resource Identifier (URI)

- Uniform Resource Locator (URL)

- Integrated Services Digital Network (ISDN) User Part (ISUP) number
- Transport address

- Email address

- Party number

- Mobile User Identity Module (UIM)

■ **Question:** What is SIP?

■ **Answer:** The Session Initiation Protocol (SIP) is an Internet Engineering Task Force (IETF) standard protocol for call signaling of VoIP, video and multimedia communication sessions.

Note: All the other parts of the session (such as call control, multimedia transport and control, and bandwidth control for point-to-point and multi-point conferences) to support the VoIP, video or multimedia communications on a packet-switched (IP) network are performed by other protocols besides SIP.

SIP was designed by Mark Handley, Henning Schulzrinne, Eve Schooler and Jonathan Rosenberg in 1996 and was standardized in 1999 by RFC 2543. SIP is a text-based protocol (similar to HTTP and SMTP text) used at layers 5 (session layer) and 7 (application layer) that is independent of the underlying TCP, UDP and Stream Control Transmission Protocol (SCTP) protocols of layer 4 (transport layer).

SIP only understands Uniform Resource Identifier (URI)-style addressing, not IP addresses or hostnames used in the H.323 protocol. A URI is a string of characters used to identify a name of a web resource. Two types of URI that you are perhaps more familiar with are the Uniform Resource Locator (URL) that uses the http or https scheme and Uniform Resource Name (URN) that uses the urn scheme. RFC 2396 defines the URI syntax which takes the form of *scheme:[//[user:password@]host[:port]][/]path[?query][#fragment]*.

SIP and H.323 are two commonly used signaling protocols for real-time voice, video and multimedia conferencing systems over IP networks. SIP takes an Internet-oriented approach (IETF) to set up and tear down multimedia communication sessions over IP, providing a client-to-server architecture that uses a centralized controlling agent, such as a Cisco Unified Communications Manager (CUCM), to route calls.

H.323, on the other hand, takes a more telecommunications-oriented approach (ITU-T) to set up and tear down voice and video over IP, providing a peer-to-peer architecture that supports user-to-user (or terminal-to-terminal) communications without the use of a centralized controlling agent.

Since the SIP text-based protocol is less defined and a more open protocol than the H.323 binary code-based protocol, every vendor can— and has in many cases—developed their own version of SIP with unique vendor-specific extensions. This can create interoperability problems between different vendor equipment using their own version of SIP.

The SIP signaling protocol is not compatible with the H.323 signaling protocol. In order to get SIP devices to communicate with H.323 devices, a gateway device is used to translate messages between the two different protocols.

- **Question:** What are the three minimum addresses that must be configured on an endpoint device that is using H.323 if these addresses are not provided by a DHCP server?
- **Answer:** (1) The endpoint IPv4 address with appropriate netmask; (2) the default gateway for the endpoint; and (3) the IPv4 address of the controlling client, such as a Cisco Unified Communications Manager (CUCM).

Note: Endpoints are the devices of a video conference or telepresence system that the end user can control. Endpoints include the devices used to make and engage in a video conference call such as a phone, PC, tablet, camera and monitor.

In telepresence or videoconferencing documentation, you will also find the term endpoint being used to identify other local devices that support the telepresence call such as a Cisco Unified Communication Manager (CUCM), Cisco Multipoint Control Unit (MCU) or a codec device. TelePresence endpoints are also referred to as TelePresence collaboration endpoints or simply endpoints.

- **Question:** What are the two most commonly used signaling protocols in video over IP?
- **Same Question:** What are the two most common signaling protocols used in multimedia teleconferencing?
- **Answer:** H.323 and Session Initiation Protocol (SIP).

- **Question:** What type of device is used to allow the SIP protocol to communicate with the H.323 protocol?
- **Answer:** A gateway device.

PROTOCOLS USED WITH TELEPRESENCE Q&A

- **Question:** What is H.320?
- **Answer:** H.320 is the International Telecommunication Union-Telecommunication Standardization Sector (ITU-T) recommendation to support VoIP, video and multimedia communication sessions on an Integrated Services Digital Network (ISDN) network.

Note: H.320 includes a suite of other protocols including H.221 (defines the structure for multimedia over one or more ISDN B-channels), H.230 (defines control and information data for multimedia), H.242 (defines call signaling), audio codecs (such as G.728, G.711 and G.722) and video codecs (such as H.261, H.262 and H.263).

- **Question:** What is H.324?

- **Answer:** H.324 is the International Telecommunication Union-Telecommunication Standardization Sector (ITU-T) recommendation to support VoIP, video and multimedia communication sessions over low-bit-rate circuit-switched networks such as ordinary analog telephone lines in the plain old telephone system (POTS).

Note: With the appropriate gateway device, H.324 systems can interoperate with other systems such as LANs, IP, ATM or ISDN networks.

- **Question:** What is H.239
- **Answer:** H.239 allows participants of a teleconference call to see not only the participants, but also computer data and images along with video streams at the same time on the teleconference monitor or screen.

Note: In 2003, the ITU-T made the H.239 recommendation after Norwegian electronics manufacturer, Tandberg, produced a way to send computer or video presentations along with a video teleconference session in 2000. H.239, also titled "Role management and additional media channels for H.3xx-series terminals", is an ITU-T recommendation for multimedia communications, such as teleconferencing and video presentation, occurring simultaneously over various networks within a single call session.

- **Question:** What is E.164?
- **Answer:** H.164 is the protocol used for the international telephone numbering system.

Note: H.164, also titled "The international public telecommunication numbering plan" is an ITU-T recommendation for defining a numbering plan for the world-wide public switched telephone network (PSTN)—in other words, the international telephone numbering system we use today.

- **Question:** What is H.264?
- **Answer:** H.264 is an ITU-T video compression standard used for recording, compression and distribution of video content only.

Note: H.264 is also known as MPEG-4 Part 10 and Advanced Video Coding (MPEG-4 AVC or simply AVC). H.264 is a block-oriented motion-compensation-based video compression standard for recording, compression and distribution of video content. AVC looks at video in blocks or frames to identify redundant pixels that are replaced (compensated) with a short description for each original pixel to reduce the size of video traffic.

As a result, H.264 can convert a variety of multimedia—such as digital TV, DVD-video, mobile TV, videoconferencing and Internet video streaming—into a compressed format that takes up less bandwidth when stored or transmitted. If you ever downloaded recorded or live streaming videos or watched a video on a Blu-ray disc, chances are your video was compressed using H.264 or its successor, H.265.

Many codec devices use the H.264 standard for recording, compression and distribution of video content. All Cisco TelePresence endpoints support H.264.

- **Question:** What is H.265?
- **Answer:** H.265 is an ITU-T video compression standard used for recording, compression and distribution of video content only, and provides twice the compression efficiency of H.264.

Note: H.265, also known as MPEG-H Part 2 and High Efficiency Video Coding (HEVC), was published in 2015. The first version of H.265 (Part

1) was published in 2013 as a successor to H.264. H.265 provides twice the compression ratio of H.264 video quality that is equal to or better than the video quality of H.264. This provides smaller file sizes than H.264 without loss in video quality.

There are still many older H.264 playback devices or older PCs out there which cannot decode the newer H.265 compressed video. Therefore, H.264 will still be relevant until users replace their H.264 playback machines with a playback device that is compatible with H.265.

- **Question:** What is MPEG2?
- **Answer:** MPEG2 is a lossy compression protocol commonly used for recording, compression and distribution of video and audio content.

Note: Moving Pictures Expert Group version 2 (MPEG-2) is a widely used compression standard that uses lossy compression to store and transmit video and audio content on DVDs, over-the-air ATSC digital TV, satellite TV and cable TV broadcasting.

MPEG-2 was developed by Moving Pictures Expert Group (MPEG); is defined by ITU-T as H.222/H.262; and is an international standard under International Organization for Standardization (ISO)/International Electrotechnical Commission (IEC) 13818.

Lossy compression, also known as irreversible compression, is a less efficient method of reducing the file size of images, recorded and streaming video and audio through the use of inexact approximations and partial data discarding of the original content that produces coarser content presentation than more efficient methods such as H.264 and H.265. When lossy compression reaches the point to where distortions in the image or video are noticeable by the viewer, those distortions are called artifacts.

However, lossy compression can significantly reduce files sizes without degrading the content to a noticeably undesirable quality to users. For this reason, lossy compression is commonly used for video and audio content, while lossless compression is typically used for data and text files.

- **Question:** What is JPEG2k?
- **Answer:** JPEG 2000 is a compression protocol for still images created by the JPEG committee to replace the original JPEG format.

Note: Joint Photographic Experts Group 2000 (JPEG2k) was created by the JPEG committee in 2000 to replace the original JEPG protocol introduced in 1992. The JPEG committee consists of ISO/IEC JTC1 and ITU-T. JPEG uses the .jpg filename extension, while JPEG2k uses the .jp2 filename extension.

JPEG2k seems to provide little advantage over JPEG in image quality at high bit rates; however, at lower bit rates, JPEG2k provides more noticeable image quality over JPEG. What JPEG2k lacks in large improvements over JPEG in image quality, it makes up for in providing greater image resolution presentations of the decoded image.

The small gains in compression efficiency of JPEG2k over JPEG seems to account for the small traction in gaining acceptance in the market by manufactures to date—they are still making many devices today with the original JPEG compression. Both JPEG and JPEG2k provide lossy and lossless compression—with the lossy compression appearing at times just as good as the lossless compression.

There is also a video version of JPEG2k, called Motion JPEG 2000, that is a commonly used standard for digital cinema movies at theaters.

- **Question:** What is Jabber?

- **Answer:** Jabber is a communications protocol based on Extensible Markup Language (XML) used as an instant messaging platform. The Cisco Jabber is a soft phone for mobile devices with capabilities for telepresence, IM, voice, HD video, voice messaging, desktop sharing and conferencing.

Note: Jabber was originally developed by the Jabber open-source community in 1999 for near real-time instant messaging (IM), presence information and contact list maintenance. Jeremie Miller, who started working on Jabber technology in 1998, released the first version of Jabber, called the jabberd server, in 1999. In 2004, Jabber was redefined as Extensible Messaging and Presence Protocol (XMPP) in RFC 3920. The Jabber.org that was started in 1999 is still offering free XMPP accounts to users today.

In 2008, Cisco Systems acquired Jabber, Inc. Cisco Jabber is integrated with Microsoft Office and can be used on a variety of mobile devices such as an iPhone or tablet for anywhere, anytime communication or collaboration via chat, voice, video calls or multiparty conferences. The Cisco Jabber registers to the Cisco Unified Communications Manager (CUCM). The Cisco Jabber Video for TelePresence registers to the Cisco Video Communications Server (VCS).

- **Question:** What DHCP option does video endpoints use to locate a server in order to download their configuration?
- **Answer:** DHCP option 150.

Note: Dynamic Host Configuration Protocol (DHCP) uses configuration option code numbers between 0 and 255. Option 150 is Cisco proprietary and allows you to define the IPv4 addresses of TFTP servers—such as a Cisco Unified Communications Manager (CUCM) or Cisco Unified Communications Manager Express (CME)—so that IP phones or telepresence endpoint devices can locate the TFTP server (CUCM or CME) in order to download their configuration file so they can communicate with the CUCM or CME.

Non-Cisco devices use IEEE standard option 66 for the same purpose—RFC 2132 defines option 66. Besides the Cisco proprietary 150 and open standard 66 differences, DHCP option 150 supports a list of TFTP servers, each with their own IP address; while DHCP option 66 supports only the IP address or hostname of a single TFTP server.

DHCP options 150 and 66 for telepresence endpoints is similar to DHCP option 43 for wireless devices—option 43 allows wireless access points (APs) to find available wireless LAN controllers (WLCs) in order to download their configuration file in order to communicate with the WLC.

- **Question:** What is Binary Floor Control Protocol (BFCP)?
- **Answer:** The BFCP protocol controls which telepresence endpoint users are allowed to share and access presentations and desktops during a video conversation.

Note: In 2006, Binary Floor Control Protocol (BFCP) was defined in RFC 4582 to be used within a conference to manage access to a set of shared resources such as the right to send media to a particular media session or the right to access shared media resources. BFCP is supported only on SIP networks and SIP endpoints.

ADAPTIVE BITRATE TRANSCODE Q&A

- **Question:** What is adaptive bitrate transcode?
- **Answer:** Adaptive bitrate transcode is used for streaming multimedia over HTTP across IP networks to provide the best quality multimedia streaming based on the real-time bandwidth available and the user's device capabilities.

Note: What makes adaptive bitrate streaming "adaptive" is the fact that it performs real-time detection of available bandwidth and CPU capacity of the user's network and adapts (adjusts) video streaming quality based on those factors. In other words, adaptive bitrate streaming seeks to find the balance between streaming the best bitrate and resolution for multimedia to users based on the user's network speed and the user's device capabilities. Although the bitrate of the multimedia streaming is changing and adapting according the changes in the network and the user's device, these changes are not noticed by the user. As a result, adaptive bitrate streaming provides a better overall user experience through less buffering, stuttering or noticeable audio pops, and faster start times of streaming multimedia.

A transcode is made up of an encoded video content (such as video in 1920 x 1080 resolution) that is converted (transcoded) into compressed video streams (multiple bitrates) of equal or lesser resolutions that can be transmitted across the Internet and played (playback) on a computer or mobile device.

The transcode in adaptive bitrate streaming is a package of transcodes of an Adaptive Set that covers a range of bitrates that are used for the same multimedia to help find that balance between streaming the best bitrate and resolution for multimedia across the Internet to users based on the user's network speed and the user's device capabilities.

Different user devices manufactured by different vendors all have different Adaptive Set requirements to ensure their device can receive or playback the best videos based on the packages of transcodes. What this means is video and multimedia producers have to develop multiple packages or sets of transcodes for a single video or multimedia content in order to properly display the content at the best quality for different vendor devices. Video producers may include anywhere from 20 to 40 different transcodes for a single video content so that their streaming content operates properly on user devices.

Adaptive bitrate streaming uses HTTP instead of Real-time Transport Protocol (RTP) or Real Time Streaming Protocol (RTSP) that was commonly used in the past for video streaming.

SIGNALING AND SCHEDULING STANDARDS Q&A

- **Question:** What is SCTE-35?
- **Answer:** SCTE-35 is a signaling standard used for inserting advertisements in a video stream, such as a TV program or streaming sports event.

Note: The Society of Cable Telecommunications Engineers (SCTE) along with the American National Standards Institute (ANSI) developed the SCTE-35 standard for insertion of advertisements in a video streams, referred to as digital program insertion (DPI) in broadcasts or Over-The-Top (OTT) video delivery on the Internet.

Dual-tone multi-frequency (DTMF) was originally used for inserting advertisements into analog broadcasting. Perhaps you may remember DTMF tones used on push-button telephones for signaling on analog telephone systems. Now that we're in the digital age, DTMF has been replaced with SCTE-35 to insert advertisements into digital broadcasting.

As you may know, many TV programs make their money by selling advertisement space within their broadcasting timeframe. The more viewers there are for a popular broadcast, such as the Super Bowl or some other special event, the higher the price broadcasters can charge companies to advertise during their broadcast. Two important techniques for inserting advertisements into video broadcasts are SCTE-104 and SCTE-35.

SCTE-35 allows broadcasters or video providers to insert or splice company advertisement segments, in the form of SCTE-35 packets, that are multiplexed with the video and audio packets (the main program segments) anywhere in the broadcast streams. This process is referred to as digital program insertion (DPI).

The SCTE-35 coding commands control SCTE-35 packet messages for starting and stopping splice events for ad segments within broadcasts; the duration of the ad; and the content within each ad segment. This information about the start, stop, duration and content of advertisement segments are referred to as metadata. The SCTE-35 coding commands are performed outside of the video stream and typically follow Event Signaling and Management (ESAM) and Event Scheduling and Notification Interface (ESNI) standards.

An example of SCTE-35 commands, referred to as ad insertion markers, to switch from normal broadcasting to an advertisement (a commercial break), you would set the **out_of_network_indicator** command to 1. This is referred to as a cue-out event. When switching from the ad commercial back to normal programming, the **out_of_network_indicator** command is set to **0**. This is referred to as a cue-in event.

- **Question:** What is SCTE-104?
- **Answer:** SCTE-104 is a signaling standard used for requesting the insertion of advertisements in a video stream, such as a TV program or streaming sports event.

Note: SCTE and ANSI also developed the SCTE-35 standard to insert advertisements into digital broadcasting. The main difference between SCTE-104 and SCTE-35 is that SCTE-104 makes the request for the insertion of advertisements in a video stream; SCTE-35 is the fulfillment of the request to insert those advertisements.

- **Question:** What is SCTE-224?
- **Answer:** SCTE-224 is the Event Scheduling and Notification Interface (ESNI) standard developed by SCTE to help content providers and operators format and manage digital content event scheduling and notification.

Note: SCTE-224 or Event Scheduling and Notification Interface (ESNI) is a web interface to make the life of video content programmers easier by providing an ESNI interface that reduces the laborious complexity of scheduling, formatting and managing digital content events and policy information. The ESNI interface does this by replacing the content provider's traditional manual control of digital content with an ESNI programmed interface; thus, eliminating many of the previous manual operations.

EVENT SIGNALING & MANAGEMENT (ESAM) AND SESSION DESCRIPTION PROTOCOL (SDP) Q&A

- **Question:** What is ESAM?
- **Answer:** Event Signaling and Management (ESAM) is an OpenCable specification that provides processing and packaging of video content for dynamic ad insertion standards.

Note: Event Signaling and Management (ESAM) is an OpenCable specification produced by a collaborative effort led by CableLabs for cable service providers and their customers.

- **Question:** What is the Session Description Protocol (SDP)?
- **Answer:** SDP provides a way to announce, invite and negotiate the parameters needed for multimedia communication sessions, such as multimedia teleconferences, VoIP calls and streaming video.

Note: Session Description Protocol (SDP) is an IETF standard (RFC 4566) for describing steaming media communications parameters, such as media type and format, that are negotiated between endpoints to establish multimedia communication session connections. These parameters are referred to as a session profile.

SDP is not the transport protocol for multimedia communications; it is simply used to negotiate the parameters between endpoints for the multimedia communications exchange. This allows SDP to be used with different types of transport protocols for multimedia communications such as Session Announcement Protocol (SAP), Session Initiation Protocol (SIP), Real Time Streaming Protocol (RTSP) and Hypertext Transport Protocol (HTTP).

CODEC Q&A

- **Question:** What is a codec?
- **Answer:** A codec is a device that encodes and decodes data streams or signals. It encodes data steams or signals into a compressed format during transmission and decodes or converts the compressed format back into an uncompressed format during reception or playback.

Note: The name "codec" is a combination of two terms—coder (for encode) and decoder. Many codec devices use ITU-T H.264 video compression standard, also known as MPEG-4 Part 10, Advanced Video Coding (MPEG-4 AVC), that is used for recording, compression and distribution of video content.

Codec devices are commonly used in voice over IP (VoIP) and video over IP applications such as videoconferencing, streaming media and video editing applications. Cisco TelePresence codec devices are used for network and multimedia interconnection and integration—LAN, camera and camera control, microphone, loudspeaker, video inputs/outputs, audio inputs/outputs, HDMI, serial and other ports.

A more simpler version of a codec is your home stereo and entertainment system that provides many of these same connections. You can access most codec devices through either a codec web GUI or the CLI or Application Programmer Interface (API) commands on the codec COM port.

MULTIPOINT, MULTIWAY AND MULTISITE Q&A

- **Question:** What is the difference between Multipoint, Multiway and Multisite conferencing?
- **Answer:** Following are the differences between Multisite, Multiway and Multipoint conferencing:

  - Multipoint is simply an industry-wide term describing multiple (three or more) endpoint devices participating in a single conference call.

Note: Multipoint video conference calls can be compared to the use of multiple voice conference calls used in the plain old telephone system (POTS).

  - Multiway is a Cisco TelePresence feature that allows users of endpoints devices to transfer (escalate) an established point-to-point call to a Cisco Multipoint Control Unit (MCU) to allow multiple endpoints to join the call.

Note: The Cisco Multiway feature allows you to scale to a large number of endpoint participants in a single conference call. There are three requirements for the Cisco Multiway feature to work:

(1) Cisco TelePresence endpoints must support Multiway.

(2) The Cisco TelePresence Video Communication Server (VCS) must be used.

(3) The Cisco TelePresence Multipoint Control Unit (MCU) must be used.

- Multisite is the name of the option key on a Cisco endpoint device allowing the device multipoint capability for up to only four participating endpoints (3+1 participants) without the use of a Cisco MCU or VCS—either of the two point-to-point endpoint devices initiating the Multisite call will host the call instead of an MCU.

Note: You must use Cisco's Multiway feature if you want to connect more than four endpoints in a single conference call. You cannot escalate an established Multisite call to a Multiway or Cisco Multipoint Control Unit (MCU) call—you must already be in the Multiway call. You cannot use Multiway and Multisite on an endpoint device at the same time.

- **Question:** What are three requirements for multiway?
- **Answer:** There are three requirements for the Cisco Multiway feature to work: (1) Cisco TelePresence endpoints must support Multiway; (2) the Cisco TelePresence Video Communication Server (VCS) must be used; and (3) the Cisco TelePresence Multipoint Control Unit (MCU) must be used.

- **Question:** What two Cisco devices are required for an endpoint to use the multiway feature?
- **Answer:** The Cisco TelePresence Video Communication Server (VCS) and the Cisco TelePresence Multipoint Control Unit (MCU).

CONFERENCE BRIDGE Q&A

- **Question:** What is a conference bridge?
- **Answer:** A conference bridge allows three or more people (multiparty) in different locations to participate in a single multimedia conference call over a packet switched network such as an IP network.

Note: Conference bridges are also referred to as a telepresence system or collaboration system; and each device in the conference bridge network are given a variety of names based on the vendor or manufacturer. The conference bridge can allow hundreds of participants in a single multimedia conference or virtual meeting room if needed. Conference bridges can also support several different multiparty conferences occurring simultaneously.

One conference bridge can also call into another conference bridge, a process called cascading, to allow the participants of one multimedia conference to see, hear and communicate with the participants of another multimedia conference. An example of a conference bridge is the Cisco Multipoint Control Unit (MCU).

- **Question:** What is cascading?
- **Answer:** Cascading is when one conference bridge, such as a Cisco Multipoint Control Unit (MCU), calls another conference bridge to allow the participants of one multimedia (telepresence) conference to see, hear and communicate with the participants of another multimedia conference.

TELEPRESENCE MANAGEMENT DEVICES Q&A

- **Question:** What Cisco devices can be used to manage a Cisco TelePresence system?
- **Same Question:** What Cisco management devices can be used to provision and schedule a TelePresence system?

- **Same Question:** What Cisco management devices can be used to provision and schedule a video conference?
- **Answer:** The following are the Cisco telepresence management systems that allow you to deploy, configure, control, manage, schedule and monitor your local or remote videoconferencing network and local and remote telepresence devices from one centralized platform.

  - Cisco Unified Communications Manager (CUCM)

  - Cisco Unified Communications Manager Express (CME)

  - Cisco TelePresence Management Suite (TMS)

  - Cisco TelePresence Manager

- **Question:** What is the Cisco Unified Communications Manager (CUCM)?
- **Answer:** The CUCM is a call-routing device providing centralized command and control to configure, setup, manage, teardown and monitor voice and video communications in a converged network.

Note: Other features on the CUCM include a host-based intrusion prevention system (HIPS) and a DHCP server to provide IP addresses to IP telephony devices.

The CUCM operating system is based on Red Hat Linux. The CUCM was formally called the Cisco Call Manager. The CUCM is also referred to as the Cisco UCM, Unified CM or UCM.

The CUCM can be deployed as a hardware, software or virtual solution in the form of the public cloud, private cloud, on-premises, remote or hybrid. You can access the CUCM either through a Web GUI or CLI commands.

CUCM uses either SIP or SCCP—not H.323—to communicate with Cisco IP phones for call setup, teardown and additional service features, such as call forwarding or conferencing, requested by the IP phones. Once the IP call is setup, CUCM is no longer involved with the call between the IP phones—the phones use Real-Time Transport Protocol (RTP) to communicate audio with each other.

- **Question:** What is the Cisco Unified Communications Manager Express (CME)?
- **Answer:** The CME is used to simplify a branch office's transition from a legacy telephone system to a modern unified communications and collaboration system.

Note: Cisco Unified Communications Manager Express (CME) was formerly called Cisco Unified CallManager Express. The Cisco CME is integrated into the IOS software of Cisco routers as a call-processing application that allows branch networks to scale and customize their transition solution from legacy telephone systems in a simple and affordably way. The router serves as both the gateway and CME for IP phones and other phone devices at the branch office.

- **Question:** What is a Cisco TelePresence Management Suite (TMS)?
- **Answer:** The Cisco TMS is a software portal that can be installed on a device, such as a physical or virtual server, that allows you to provision, deploy, configure, control, manage, schedule and monitor your local or remote videoconferencing network and telepresence devices from one centralized platform.

Note: TMS supports both H.323 and SIP signaling protocols, but not interworking between these two protocols. TMS allows telepresence administrators to manage a telepresence network to include supporting rapid, large-scale deployments of up to 100,000 Cisco TelePresence users, endpoints and soft clients; setting up user permissions; registering telepresence devices; scheduling telepresence conferences with One

Button to Push (OBTP) capability for quick conference scheduling; SMTP email event notification; troubleshooting telepresence problems; and backup and restore of endpoint configurations.

Cisco TMS stores all of its operational, system and customer data in its SQL database named "tmsng". The TMS consists of the following components:

- **Internet Information Services (IIS) Server with webapps:** Since TMS was developed using the Microsoft .NET platform, the TMS uses a Microsoft ISS server as TMS's primary web server when hosting web content, web services and web applications for users. Web-related files are stored on the Microsoft ISS server.

- **TMS Services:** The TMS services consist of the following five service components:

  - **tms:** Provides the authenticated web application viewed by users accessing the TMS. The authentication process is performed by a Microsoft ISS server.
  - **tms/public:** Provides a web application and directory structure for all web content and web services without authentication.

  - **external:** Used primarily for external-facing APIs for server integrations, external provides a web application and directory structure for all web content and web services with authentication at the web server level.

  - **cdm and pwx:** Used for hardcoded URLs.

  - **tmsagent:** Provides proxy services between endpoints and the TMS Provisioning Extension.

- **tmsng SQL Database:** The location where TMS stores all of its operational, system and customer data—in its Microsoft SQL database server named "tmsng".

- **TMS Tools application:** Used to modify database connection settings. You can access TMS Tools application from the **Start** menu on the TMS.

- **Question:** What is the Cisco TelePresence Management Suite Provisioning Extension (TMSPE)?
- **Answer:** TMSPE is an extension for the Cisco TelePresence Management Suite (TMS) and Cisco TelePresence Management Suite (TMS, version 13.2 and later) used in large-scale deployments to allow TMS to rapidly provision telepresence users, endpoints and Collaboration Meeting Rooms (CMRs).

- **Question:** What is the Cisco TelePresence Management Suite Extension for Microsoft Exchange (TMSXE)?
- **Answer:** Cisco TMSXE is an extension for the Cisco TelePresence Management Suite (TMS) that allows you to schedule Cisco TelePresence through Microsoft Outlook.

Note: Cisco TMSXE replicates scheduled meetings between Cisco TMS and Microsoft Exchange room calendars. There is no need for special software or add-ins to the Microsoft Outlook client. Cisco TMSXE works with Microsoft Exchange Server 2013, 2010, 2007 and Online (Office 365).

- **Question:** What is the Cisco TelePresence Video Communications Server (VCS)?

- **Answer:** The Cisco TelePresence Video Communications Server (VCS) is used for video call and session control, registrations and enhanced security for Cisco TelePresence conferences.

Note: The Cisco Video Communications Server is also referred to as the Cisco TelePresence Server. VCS supports both H.323 and SIP signaling protocols in addition to interworking between these two protocols. The Cisco TelePresence Video Communications Server (VCS) consists of two devices: the VCS-Control (VCS-C) device and the VCS-Expressway (VCS-E) device. The VCS-Control is used for TelePresence traffic within or inside the enterprise. When Telepresence is needed outside an enterprise, the VCS-Expressway device is used in conjunction with the VCS-Control device.

Figure 4-2 shows how the VCS-C and VCS-E can be deployed when an enterprise needs videoconferencing both within and outside the enterprise.

Figure 4-2 *Cisco VCS-Control and VCS-Expressway used for TelePresence sessions*

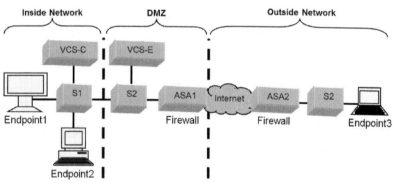

The VCS-Control is used to provide SIP registration and SIP proxy service, H.323 gatekeeper and interoperability between SIP and H.323 endpoints, zone and bandwidth management, dial-plan and call-routing control, authentication, policy services and security.

The VCS-Expressway is used to traverse the firewall, providing policy services, firewall traversal services using SIP or H.460.18/19, interworking between SIP and H.323, and Traversal Using Relays for NAT (TURN) relay services.

The Cisco TelePresence Video VCS-C and VCS-E can be deployed as a standalone or in clusters physically as an appliance or as a virtualized application on VMware with additional support for Cisco Unified Computing System (UCS) platforms.

- ■ **Question:** What is a Cisco Digital Media Manager?
- ■ **Answer:** The Cisco Digital Media Manager is the web-based central management application that allows you to manage, schedule and publish Cisco Digital Media Suite products.

Note: Cisco Digital Media Suite products include Cisco Digital Signs, Cisco Cast, Cisco Show and Share, Cisco Digital Media Encoder and the Cisco Digital Media Player.

The Cisco Digital Signs and Cisco Cast delivers digital media to displays. Cisco Digital Signs or Signage takes the concept of paper signs to a whole new level of an interactive and dynamic digital portal to information, comprehensive media and real-time collaboration.

The Cisco Cast is a business IPTV application that delivers real-time live and on-demand video and broadcast TV channels over IP to digital screens. The Cisco Cast uses the same hardware and management platform as the Cisco Digital Signs, and can either be used with Cisco Digital Signs or as its own standalone application.

Cisco Show and Share is used within an organization's network for private and highly secure webcasting and video sharing application for business videos, information, workflows, files and collaboration tools. The Cisco Show and Share delivers digital media through the web to the desktop.

- **Question:** What is a PTZ camera?
- **Answer:** The pan-tilt-zoom (PTZ) camera is a remote camera whose directional movement—such as pan left or right, tilt up or down or zoom in or out—can be controlled remotely.

Note: PTZ cameras use VISCA, a professional camera control protocol designed by Sony. The VISCA protocol and cable use the same RS232 serial communications that allows you to connect to terminal emulation software the same way you would connect to other Cisco, Telco, Juniper or Extreme network devices. In other words, your terminal emulation settings for connecting to the PTZ camera would be 9600 bits/second, no hardware flow control, 8-bit ASCII, no stop bits and 1 parity bit.
The Far-End Camera Control (FECC) feature is used to allow another user to take control of your PTZ camera. A variety of connectors can be used with the VISCA cable such as DB-9, 8-pin DIN, RJ45 and RJ11.

- **Question:** What is medianet?
- **Answer:** Medianet, in the context of Cisco Medianet, is Cisco's recommended end-to-end network architectural concept for video and collaboration deployments.

Note: The goal of Cisco's Medianet recommendation is providing a good quality video and collaboration experience for users, and providing an architectural approach that makes deploying and managing telepresence networks easier with lower risks and less costs. Cisco Medianet technologies provides four important solutions or functionality to the ever-growing multimedia conferencing and collaboration technology:

- **Autoconfiguration:** Reduces the hands-on effort and costs for endpoint moves, adds and changes.

- **Media Monitoring:** Greater vision of the telepresence network end-to-end to support management, growth and troubleshooting of the telepresence network.

- **Media Awareness:** Creates a telepresence network that is more application and context aware end-to-end to support endpoints and applications for optimal quality of experience (QoE) for telepresence users, administrators and engineers.

- **Media Services Interface (MSI):** Cisco Medianet uses the Media Services Interface (MSI), a software component embedded in Cisco video endpoints and collaboration applications that support medianet functionality.

CISCO TELEPRESENCE DEVICES Q&A

- **Question:** What is the Cisco Expressway?
- **Answer:** The Cisco Expressway provides firewall-traversal for enterprise collaboration boundaries reaching remote and mobile endpoints such as Cisco IP phones, collaboration devices, business-to-business (B2B) communications, and Jabber for smartphones, tablets and desktops. The Cisco Expressway provides private and secure communications over a public network, such as the Internet, without having to go through a VPN solution.

Note: Both the Cisco Expressway-Core device and Cisco Expressway-Edge device are used for Cisco Expressway, and are used with the Cisco Unified Communication Manager (CUCM), Cisco Business Edition or the Cisco Hosted Collaboration solution (HCS) for call control as shown Figure 4-3.

Figure 4-3 *Deployment of Cisco Expressway-Core and Cisco Expressway-Edge*

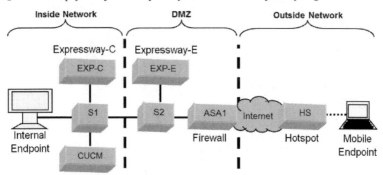

The Cisco Expressway-Core device must be in the same subnet as the CUCM, Cisco Business Edition or HCS—a VLAN can easily accomplish this requirement. The Cisco Expressway-Core is the same as Cisco TelePresence Video Communications Server (VCS)-Core (VCS-C); only Cisco Expressway-Core is deployed as a Mobile and Remote Access proxy only.

The Cisco Expressway-Edge is also referred to as Collaboration Edge. The Cisco Expressway-Edge is the same as Cisco TelePresence Video Communications Server-Expressway (VCS-E); only Cisco Expressway-Edge is deployed as a Mobile and Remote Access proxy only. In fact, Cisco Expressway-Core and Cisco Expressway-Edge use the exact same software as the VCS-C and VCS-E, respectively. You can deploy the Cisco Expressway as an appliance or virtual software.

- **Question:** What is the Cisco TelePresence Multipoint Switch?
- **Answer:** The Cisco TelePresence Multipoint Switch (CTMS) is a software that performs the same function as the Multipoint Control Unit (MCU)—it used in videoconferencing to connect multiple endpoint devices or gateways so they can participate in a single multipoint conference session, and manages and controls the multipoint conference traffic from the centralized CTMS device.

Note: The Cisco TelePresence Multipoint Switch (CTMS) reached its end-of-life on July 29, 2013 and end-of-sale on January 27, 2014. A Multipoint Control Unit (MCU) can be used instead of the CMTS.

- **Question:** What is the Cisco TelePresence Touch device?
- **Answer:** The Cisco TelePresence Touch devices are handheld devices that allow a user to actually touch or swipe their finger on or across the device's screen in a similar fashion as you would touch or swipe your iPhone or iPad screen. With Cisco's Touch devices, you can start or stop a telepresence session, share content, navigate through contact lists and directories as well as access video or voicemail messages—all with a touch or swipe of a finger.

Note: There are two types of Cisco Touch models; the Touch 8 and Touch 10. The Touch 8 has an 8-inch screen and supports the Cisco TelePresence EX90. The Touch 10 has a 10-inch screen and supports the Cisco TelePresence MX, SX and IX series.

- **Question:** What is a Cisco Digital Media Encoder (DME)?
- **Answer:** Cisco Digital Media Encoders capture and digitizes digital media for live and on-demand transmission across an IP network.

Note: The Digital Media Encoders can be managed locally or remotely and uses a variety of encoding formats, inputs and monitoring functions.

- **Question:** What is a Cisco Digital Media Player (DMP)?
- **Answer:** Cisco Digital Media Players is an endpoint device used for video decoding and playback of digital media content across digital displays for live broadcasts or on-demand video, Flash animations, text tickers and other web content.

Note: The Cisco DMP is a critical component of Cisco Digital Signs and Cisco Cast applications. Several Cisco Digital Media Players have reached end-of-life and end-of-sale.

- **Question:** What is the Cisco TelePresence Content Server (TCS)?
- **Answer:** The TelePresence Content Server (TCS) is used to record, transform, store and share Cisco TelePresence and third-party videoconferencing meetings and multimedia presentations for live broadcast and on-demand steaming access.

Note: The TCS allows you to capture, transform, store and share lectures, training sessions, meeting and any critical events for real-time live or later on-demand viewing. TCS works with SIP, H.323, H.261, H.263 and H.264 protocols. You can use the TCS as a standalone or cluster up to 10 TCS servers. Another Cisco device that performs similar functions as the TCS is the Cisco Media Experience Engine (MXE).

- **Question:** What is a Cisco Media Experience Engine (MXE)?
- **Answer:** The Cisco Media Experience Engine (MXE) is a media transformation product that allows you to capture, transform and share videos.

Note: Another Cisco device that performs similar functions as the MXE is the Cisco TelePresence Content Server (TCS). The MXE provides three main media transformation features:

- **Any-to-any media adaptation:** Automatically adapts to recorded and live video from any incompatible formats, resolutions and speeds so you can view them on-demand or live with any playback device and application.
- **Media postproduction:** Provides professional studio-quality video features to transform videos before sharing them with your target audience. Some of these features include fades to transition in and out of video sequences, video trailers, graphic overlay

options to allow layering of a fully animated graphic on top of the source video (a process called a lower-third).

- **Cisco Pulse video analytics:** Allows you to find and view video quickly and easily during a video search. Cisco Pulse performs automatic tagging and indexing of videos so you can perform a search based on a spoken phrase or word or a certain speaker.

Wireless (WiFi) Q&A

WI-FI STANDARDS AND BASICS Q&A

- **Question:** What is the Wi-Fi Alliance?
- **Answer:** The Wi-Fi Alliance, which owns the "Wi-Fi" trademark, is the organization that certifies the testing and interoperability of IEEE 802.11 (wireless) products and promotes wireless technology.

Note: The Wi-Fi Alliance was originally formed in 1999 under the name Wireless Ethernet Compatibility Alliance (WECA) when the Institute of Electrical and Electronics Engineers (IEEE) was not prepared to perform the IEEE 802.11-compliance testing and certifying that the Wi-Fi Alliance performs today.

In 2002, WECA changed its name to Wi-Fi Alliance and includes several companies such as Cisco, Motorola, Alcatel-Lucent, Nokia and 3Com.

Some companies choose not to pay the cost of certifying their wireless products through the Wi-Fi Alliance; therefore, these products, which may be IEEE 802.11-compliant, are not allowed to use the "Wi-Fi", "Wi-Fi Alliance" or "Wi-Fi Certified" logos.

- **Question:** What is a hotspot?
- **Answer:** A hotspot is the area of coverage by a wireless network.

Note: A single wireless access point (AP), such as the wireless router in your home, can cover a range of roughly 66 feet (20 meters) indoors—the hotspot area of coverage. This hotspot range extends further when the access point is outdoors.

- **Question:** What are some of the wireless standards?
- **Same Question:** What are some of the IEEE wireless types and their frequency range?
- **Answer:** 802.11a (5GHz), 802.11b (2.4GHz), 802.11g (2.4GHz), 802.11n (2.4GHz, 5GHz) and 802.11ac (2.4GHz, 5GHz, 60GHz).

Note: Although the radio signals used in wireless communications are unlicensed frequency bands, the Institute of Electrical and Electronics Engineers (IEEE) set some standards for the use of those wireless radio frequencies. IEEE defined the 802.11a and 802.11b standards in 1999. 802.11g was released in 2003, 802.11n was released in 2009, and 802.11ac was released in 2013.

- **Question:** What is WiMAX?
- **Answer:** Worldwide Interoperability for Microwave Access (WiMAX) is a Wi-Fi industry coalition that promotes and certifies the IEEE 802.16 standards for wireless broadband up to 30 miles.

Note: IEEE 802.16, deployed worldwide in 2009, is broadband wireless metropolitan area networks (WirelessMAN), referred to as Worldwide Interoperability for Microwave Access (WiMAX) by the WiMAX Forum industry alliance.

You could view the WiMAX Forum industry alliance that promotes and certifies the compatibility and interoperability of Wi-Fi products based on IEEE 802.16 standards in similar fashion to the Metro Ethernet Forum (MEF) that promotes and certifies the compatibility and interoperability of Ethernet over WAN devices.

With a range of 30 miles, WirelessMAN (IEEE 802.16 WiMAX) can provide a viable last mile technology for multimedia applications over Wi-Fi networks, providing a cheaper solution that is quicker and easier to deploy than other Ethernet, fiber or copper cable solutions.

- **Question:** Are wireless networks full-duplex or half-duplex networks?
- **Answer:** Half-duplex.

Note: Since Wi-Fi is half-duplex, it uses carrier-sense multiple access with collision avoidance (CSMA/CA) to avoid collisions during transmissions. Wi-Fi with Multiple-Input Multiple-Output (MIMO) may use multiple transmitters and receivers to transfer more data at the same time, but this is still half-duplex.

- **Question:** What is frequency?
- **Answer:** Frequency is the number of repeating waveform cycles in a second, and is measured in hertz (Hz).

Note: Hertz (Hz) , named after the German physicist Heinrich Rudolf Hertz who first proved the existence of electromagnetic waves, is simply a unit of measure for frequency defined as one cycle per second. In Figure 5-1, the 1Hz frequency waveform, also known as a sine wave, on the left has only one cycle per second. The 5Hz frequency waveform on the right has five cycles per second—it repeats itself five times in a second.

Figure 5-1 *Cycles per second in different frequencies*

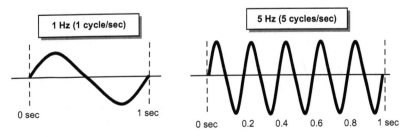

In radio frequency, and in Wi-Fi (also spelled "WiFi") frequencies in particular, we have billions of repeating cycles per second. Therefore, we use Gigahertz (GHz) to represent billions of hertz (Giga comes from the Greek word *gigas* meaning giant). So when you see frequencies such as 2.4GHz, 5GHz or 60GHz in Wi-Fi, it is referring to the number of cycles per second—2.4 billion, 5 billion or 60 billion cycles per second, respectively.

The higher the frequency range, such as 5GHz or 60GHz, the higher the data rates possible. Unfortunately, there is a tradeoff with these higher data rates in that higher frequencies also have shorter ranges of signal strength than lower frequencies such as 2.4GHz.

Some wireless routers are single band meaning they only use a single frequency such as 802.11a (5GHz) only, 802.11b (2.4GHz) only or 802.11g (2.4GHz) only. Dual band wireless routers can use two different frequencies simultaneously such as 802.11n (2.4GHz, 5GHz) or 802.11ac (2.4GHz, 5GHz, 60GHz). Dual band Wi-Fi allows you to have wireless connections for devices that use the old 2.4GHz frequency while using the 5GHz for newer devices that use only 5GHz.

- **Question:** What is bandwidth?
- **Answer:** Bandwidth is a range or the width of multiple different frequencies measured in hertz (Hz).

Note: Bandwidth determines the width of the range of radio frequencies that make up the bandwidth. Just as an airplane's first class and economy class determine the width of the seats, the higher the bandwidth number, the wider the range of frequencies that can sit within that bandwidth.

Bandwidth, also referred to as frequency band or band, is measured from the lowest frequency to the highest frequency in a continuous set of different frequencies. For example, the frequency range of our human voice, called voice frequency, is approximately 300 hertz (300Hz) at the lowest voice range to 3400 hertz (3.4KHz) at the highest voice range. To find the "bandwidth" of the human voice, subtract 300Hz from 3400Hz, and the difference equals 3100Hz bandwidth. (In telephony, the Nyquist theorem is used to sample voice signals at a rate of 8KHz (twice the highest voice frequency) to provide enough samplings to effectively reconstruct the voice signal at the distant end.)

Every bandwidth has a center frequency, also called the nominal frequency, which is the middle frequency of the bandwidth. The center frequency of the human voice frequency range (bandwidth) of 3100Hz is 1550Hz (3100 divided by 2 equals 1550). Figure 5-2 shows a depiction of the frequency range (bandwidth) of the human voice—300Hz to 3400Hz. (The number of cycles in the drawing were limited for simplicity.)

Figure 5-2 *Voice frequency range (bandwidth) of the human voice*

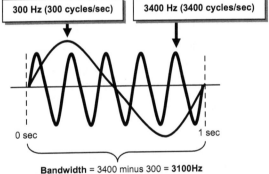

300 Hz (300 cycles/sec) 3400 Hz (3400 cycles/sec)

0 sec   1 sec

Bandwidth = 3400 minus 300 = **3100Hz**

- **Question:** What bandwidth is used to measure Wi-Fi radio signals?
- **Answer:** Bandwidth in Wi-Fi technology is measured in megahertz (MHz) or millions of hertz.

Note: IEEE 802.11a (5GHz frequency) has a bandwidth of 20MHz; 802.11b (2.4GHz frequency) has a 22MHz bandwidth; 802.11g (2.4GHz frequency) has a 20MHz bandwidth; 802.11n (2.4GHz and 5GHz frequencies) uses both a 20MHz and 40MHz bandwidth; and 802.11ac (2.4GHz, 5GHz and 60GHz frequencies) uses several bandwidths— 20MHz, 40MHz, 80MHz and 160MHz bandwidths. Figure 5-3 shows that an 80MHz bandwidth in 802.11ac is a much wider bandwidth than a 20MHz bandwidth in 802.11a.

Figure 5-3 *Differences in widths of bandwidths*

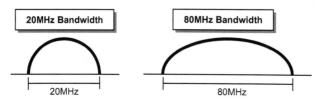

- **Question:** What type of modulation does 802.11a, 802.11g, 802.11n and 802.11ac use?
- **Answer:** Orthogonal Frequency-Division Multiplexing (OFDM).

Note: Modulation is a technique where a carrier radio signal is used to carry information signals (data, video or voice) while the information signals are sent from transmitter to receiver. Some of the older and more commonly used modulation techniques are amplitude modulation (AM) and frequency modulation (FM) such as in your AM and FM radio stations.

In wireless networks, modulation techniques such as OFDM or Direct-Sequence Spread Spectrum (DSSS) are used. 802.11b uses DSSS modulation. OFDM is widely used in both wired and wireless digital communications applications such as digital subscriber line (DSL); digital radio and TV broadcasts; Data Over Cable Service Interface Specification (DOCSIS) 3.1; power-line communication (PLC), also known as broadband over power lines (BPL) when PLC is used for Internet access; and wireless networks.

OFDM uses frequency division multiplexing (FDM) in order to use multiple subcarrier frequencies to carry information. Each subcarrier frequency is orthogonal to all the other subcarrier frequencies in the set of multiplexed frequency signals. In other words, each subcarrier frequency in OFDM has a precise minimum frequency spacing required to maintain separation from each other. This prevents the multiple subcarrier frequencies used in OFDM from interfering with each other.

The difference between OFDM and FDM is that FDM uses what is called a guard band to provide this separation between multiple frequencies being multiplexed together. OFDM, on the other hand, does not need guard bands because of its orthogonal properties.

Direct-Sequence Spread Spectrum (DSSS) uses a spread spectrum modulation technique that spreads out the bandwidth of the carrier frequency to a size that is larger than what is actually needed for the information signal (data, voice or video). The idea here with DSSS is that by spreading out the carrier signal over a larger bandwidth, the excess bandwidth appears as noise, similar to white noise, that acts as a buffer from other interfering or jamming signals.

The "Direct-Sequence" in DSSS refers to the excess noise signal that is created by a pseudorandom sequence of 1 and -1 values at frequencies higher than the original voice, video or data signal. The excess noise signal is also used at the receiver end to reconstruct the original information signal.

- **Question:** What is the speed of a Wi-Fi network measured in?
- **Same Question:** What unit of measure is used for the data rate of Wi-Fi networks?
- **Answer:** The speed (data rate) of a Wi-Fi network is measured in megabits per second (Mbits/s or Mbps) or gigabits per second (Gbits/s or Gbps).

Note: Network speed is the amount of time or rate it takes for data, voice or video to travel through a network. Networking speed goes by many names such as data rate, data transfer rate, data transfer speed, data stream, stream data rate, throughput or bandwidth.

The speed (data rate) of a Wi-Fi network is measured in megabits per second (Mbits/s or Mbps) which is millions of bits per second or gigabits per second (Gbps) which is billions of bits per second. A bit is a binary digit (0 or 1) that is the smallest unit of information in a computer or network system. This is similar to the way the atom is the smallest unit of the basic building blocks of ordinary matter. Just as atoms can join together to form molecules that make up the objects around you, 0 and 1 bits can be joined together to form information, applications and processes for the computing and networking systems we use today.

Generally, the higher the bandwidth value the faster the speed (data rate) of a network. Higher frequency can also translate to faster speeds. However, the higher the frequency of a wireless network (5GHz versus 2.4GHz, for example), the less strength of the wireless signal range or its ability to penetrate walls. This disadvantage of higher frequency wireless networks may necessitate the deployment of more access points (APs) to make up for the shortfall in signal strength in each AP.

The fastest speed or maximum data rate of 802.11a is 54Mbps. Since 802.11a uses a 5GHz frequency, the strength (range) of its 54Mbps data rate is good for up to 25–75 feet indoors from the access point, depending on signal attenuation, obstructions and interference.

The maximum speed (data rate) of 802.11b is 11Mbps. However, as I just stated, the strength of each data rate is affected by the frequency it uses. Therefore, since 802.11b uses a 2.4GHz frequency, the strength of its 11Mbps data rate is good for up to 100–150 feet indoors from the access point, depending on signal attenuation, obstructions and interference.

The maximum speed (data rate) of 802.11g is 54Mbps. Since 802.11g uses a 2.4GHz frequency, the strength of its 54Mbps data rate is good for up to

100–150 feet indoors from the access point, depending on signal attenuation, obstructions and interference.

The maximum speed (data rate) of 802.11n is 150Mbps but this speed can be increased to 300Mbps, 450Mbps and 600Mbps using channel bonding. 802.11n uses both 2.4GHz and 5GHz frequencies, providing various levels of signal strengths from various distances from the access point; generally 175 feet (more or less) indoors from the access point, depending on signal attenuation, obstructions and interference.

The maximum speed (data rate) of 802.11ac could range from 866.7Mbps to 1.3Gbps. 802.11ac uses 2.4GHz, 5GHz and 60GHz frequencies, providing various levels of signal strengths from various distances from the access point; generally 175 feet (more or less) indoors from the access point, depending on signal attenuation, obstructions and interference.

Keep in mind that all of these maximum speeds are in ideal conditions. In reality, many Wi-Fi networks operate in less than ideal conditions, so you can expect these speeds (data rates) to be much slower in many places where Wi-Fi networks are deployed.

WI-FI CHANNELS Q&A

- **Question:** Why is it important to know what Wi-Fi channels are being used?
- **Same Question:** What happens when Wi-Fi channels overlap?
- **Same Question:** What happens when channels 1, 3, 6 and 11 are used in 802.11b?
- **Same Question:** How many channels can be used in in 802.11b and 802.11g Wi-Fi networks.
- **Answer:** Overlapping Wi-Fi channels cause interference between the overlapping channels. To prevent interference between Wi-Fi channels, only 3 channels (channels 1, 6 and 11) can be used in 802.11b and 802.11g Wi-Fi networks.

Note: Wi-Fi technology uses bandwidths and their respective center frequency to represent Wi-Fi channels. The center frequency in Wi-Fi is measured in megahertz (MHz). For example, 802.11b uses a total of 11 channels in the US and Canada (other countries may use up to 14 channels for 802.11b). Each of these channels have a 22MHz wide bandwidth but each 22MHz bandwidth is made up of a different range of frequencies, each with their own center frequency. Figure 5-4 shows how the 802.11b standard uses the 2.4GHz frequency with 22MHz bandwidth to produce 11 Wi-Fi channels.

Figure 5-4 *Bandwidth and channels in 802.11b (2.4GHz frequency and 22MHz bandwidth)*

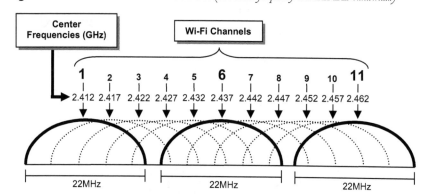

In Wi-Fi, the range of frequencies within one channel band (bandwidth) must not overlap with the range of frequencies of another bandwidth channel; otherwise, signal interference occurs. This is why only three channels—1, 6 and 11—are commonly used on wireless access points (APs) with the 2.4GHz Wi-Fi in 802.11b and 802.11g as shown in Figure 5-4. Although there are 11 channels available, channels 1, 6 and 11 are the only channels whose range of frequencies (bandwidth) do no overlap. Other countries besides the US and Canada commonly use channels 1, 5, 9 and 13 because they use 14 channels.

The disadvantage of using 2.4GHz Wi-Fi is it easily becomes a crowded radio frequency—with only three available channels—among adjacent businesses using the same three channels, resulting in interference.

Many appliances also use the 2.4GHz frequency such as microwaves, cordless phones, baby monitors, video senders and wireless speakers, causing interference with the 2.4GHz Wi-Fi signal. All of this interference translates to a decrease in range and throughput, degraded signals or complete loss of the wireless connection.

WLAN networks using 5GHz use 23 channels starting at channel 36 and ending at channel 165; but in the US, only 9 of these channels are normally used by the public—channels 36, 40, 44, 48, 149, 153, 157, 161 and 165. The 5GHz frequency experiences less interference than 2.4GHz due to more non-overlapping channels and fewer appliances operating at that frequency. Most of the other US 5GHz channels are considered Dynamic Frequency Selection (DFS) channels shared by first responders and other emergency personnel.

802.11a, 802.11n and 802.11ac use the 5GHz frequency that allows a total of 9 non-DFS, non-overlapping channel bands (channels 36, 40, 44, 48, 149, 153, 157, 161 and 165) with the 20MHz bandwidth. 802.11ac also uses the 40MHz frequency allowing 4 non-overlapping channels (out of 11 channels), 80MHz allowing 2 non-overlapping channels (out of 5 channels) and 160MHz allowing only 1 non-overlapping channel (out of 2 channels).

- ■ **Question:** How many channels are available in a wireless network and how many of these channels overlap?
- ■ **Answer:** In the US, WLAN networks using 2.4GHz use 11 channels for indoor use, of which only three channels do not overlap or interfere with each other—channels 1, 6 and 11.

WLAN networks using 5GHz use 23 channels starting at channel 36 and ending at channel 165; but in the US, only 9 of these channels are normally used by the public—channels 36, 40, 44, 48, 149, 153, 157, 161 and 165. Most of the other US 5GHz channels are considered

Dynamic Frequency Selection (DFS) channels shared by first responders and other emergency personnel.

Note: 802.11b and 802.11g use the 2.4GHz frequency. Since only channels 1, 6 and 11 of the 2.4GHz frequency do not cause interference with each other, these channels are set as the default channels on 2.4GHz wireless devices by manufacturers. This may be a welcomed setting for many businesses but if two or more business that use different WLAN networks are in close proximity to each other, it is possible their default channel settings could cause degradation of their wireless network due to overlapping conflicting frequencies of the stronger 2.4GHz signal.

The 5GHz frequency experiences less interference due to more non-overlapping channels and fewer appliances operating at that frequency. 802.11a, 802.11n and 802.11ac use the 5GHz frequency that allows a total of 9 non-DFS, non-overlapping channel bands (channels 36, 40, 44, 48, 149, 153, 157, 161 and 165) with the 20MHz bandwidth. 802.11ac also uses the 40MHz frequency allowing 4 non-overlapping channels (out of 11 channels), 80MHz allowing 2 non-overlapping channels (out of 5 channels) and 160MHz allowing only 1 non-overlapping channel (out of 2 channels).

- ■ **Question:** What is channel bonding?
- ■ **Answer:** Channel bonding is the combining of non-overlapping Wi-Fi channels for increased throughput (bandwidth) and redundancy between wireless devices.

Note: Channel bonding is also referred to as Ethernet bonding or broadband bonding. In Figure 5-4, we showed the 802.11b Wi-Fi with three non-overlapping 22MHz bandwidth channels (channels 1, 6 and 11). Channel bonding allows you to combine two or more of these channels—such as channels 1 and 6 or 6 and 11 or 1, 6 and 11—to increase the bandwidth of the Wi-Fi signal between the access point and a wireless device.

When channels 1 and 6 (which are 22MHz each) are bonded together, it produces a 44MHz bonded channel. This allows a greater throughput to transmit more data. When channels 1, 6 and 11 are bonded together, it produces a 66MHz bonded channel.

Channel bonding of a Wi-Fi network that uses only three non-overlapping channels, such as 2.4GHz, has its disadvantages in that fewer channels are available for separation between the Wi-Fi frequencies used by access points. The risk of interference increases in a Wi-Fi network that has fewer than three separate channel frequencies.

For this reason, Wi-Fi networks with more than three non-overlapping channels, such as a 5GHz Wi-Fi network that has as many as 23 channels, can benefit from channel bonding. Channel bonding is enabled by default in many 5GHz Wi-Fi networks.

BEAMFORMING Q&A

- **Question:** What is beamforming?
- **Answer:** Beamforming helps to extend the range (Wi-Fi signal strength) of higher frequency wireless signals (such as 5GHz) by focusing the beam of wireless signals. The focused beam provides a stronger wireless signal to help maintain better quality data, voice and video streaming at greater distances.

Note: The higher the frequency of a wireless network (5GHz versus 2.4GHz frequencies, for example), the less strength of the wireless signal to penetrate walls. This disadvantage of higher frequency wireless networks may necessitate the deployment of more APs to make up for the shortfall in signal strength in each access point.

The range (Wi-Fi signal strength) of the higher frequency wireless signals can be extended through beamforming. Instead of transmitting omnidirectional wireless signals, beamforming uses multiple-input, multiple-output (MIMO) technology that focuses the radio signals sent through multiple antennas of a wireless router or AP toward wireless client devices (called a beamformee) or that can reflect off of walls— rather than through walls—to extend the Wi-Fi signal's range. The focused beam provides a stronger wireless signal to help maintain better quality data, voice and video streaming at greater distances. An example of an 802.11 protocol that uses beamforming is 802.11ac.

WI-FI ROAMING Q&A

- **Question:** What is roaming?
- **Answer:** Roaming is the ability of a client mobile device to move from one access point (AP) to another access point within the same Wi-Fi network with uninterrupted access to that Wi-Fi network.

Note: Not all vendor model access points support roaming. There are two types of roaming: layer 2 roaming and layer 3 roaming. In layer 2 roaming, all of the access points within the same Wi-Fi network use the same SSID, VLAN and IP subnet. In layer 3 roaming, also known as mobile IP, all of the access points within the same Wi-Fi network use the same SSID but with possibly different VLANs and different IP subnets.

- **Question:** What is a mobility group?
- **Answer:** A mobility group is a group of Wireless LAN Controllers (WLCs) that use the same mobility group name that supports wireless device roaming.

Note: As its name suggests, a mobility group supports mobility or roaming of Wi-Fi devices. WLCs grouped together in a mobility group share wireless client device information; forwarding of traffic from roaming Wi-Fi devices; and provide redundancy among the WLCs within the mobility group.

WI-FI ANTENNAS, PROBES AND BEACONS Q&A

- **Question:** What are the two main types of antennas used in Wi-Fi?
- **Answer:** Omnidirectional and directional.

- **Question:** What type of wireless antennas are used indoors?
- **Answer:** Omnidirectional or multiple-input, multiple-output (MIMO) antennas.

Note: Omnidirectional antennas transmit in all directions. When wireless antennas are mounted on ceilings indoors, the radio waves transmit downward in a 360 degree direction. Instead of transmitting omnidirectional, some wireless devices use beamforming to focus the wireless signal in a particular direction.

Beamforming uses multiple-input, multiple-output (MIMO) technology that focuses the radio signals sent through multiple antennas of a wireless router or AP toward wireless client devices (called a beamformee) or that can reflect off of walls—rather than through walls— to extend or focus the Wi-Fi signal's range of the higher frequency (5GHz) signals. An example of an 802.11 protocol that uses beamforming is 802.11ac.

Another antenna that's been in use for years before MIMO antennas is directional antennas. Like MIMO antennas, directional antennas can focus the wireless radio signal in a particular direction. A directional antenna used on an access point (AP) will cause the circumference of the wireless radio signal to cover the area in front of where the antenna is pointed while the back of the antenna gets little to no radio frequency coverage.

- **Question:** What is the difference between a probe and a beacon?
- **Answer:** The probe signal is transmitted by a client wireless device to locate an access point to connect to the Wi-Fi network. The access

point uses a beacon signal to respond back to the client wireless device to identify the name of the Wi-Fi network.

Note: When a client wireless device sends out a probe looking for a WLAN network to connect to, each access point within the range of that client wireless device will respond back with a beacon containing the Service Set ID (SSID) assigned to that access point. These SSIDs are displayed as a list of Wi-Fi network names you see on your mobile device when you are seeking to connect to a Wi-Fi network in your area.

When multiple APs using the same SSID send back a beacon with the same SSID to your wireless device, your wireless device will select the beacon with the strongest signal and display that access point's SSID and signal strength on your wireless device. Once you log into that AP with your wireless device, the AP will add the MAC address of your wireless device to its association table and begin providing your wireless device access to its Wi-Fi network.

WI-FI INTERFERENCE AND COLLISIONS Q&A

- **Question:** What are sources of interference for wireless networks?
- **Same Question:** What are some common problems that cause congestion or disruptions on a wireless network?
- **Answer:** The 2.4GHz Wi-Fi frequency easily becomes crowded by other competing devices using the same 2.4GHz, such as adjacent businesses using the same three channels (1, 6 and 11) in their WLAN network; microwave ovens; cordless phones, baby monitors and video cameras; wireless speakers; motion detectors, wireless security cameras and other video feeds; and amateur radio signals. Physical objects can also cause interference by either reflecting or absorbing the Wi-Fi radio signal. Among objects, metal objects provide the highest amount of interference to Wi-Fi networks.

Note: A simple oversight that can cause interference to the Wi-Fi network is when two businesses located close to each other have different WLANs that use the same 2.4Ghz radio frequency on their access points—a common problem with adjacent Wi-Fi networks using 802.11b or 802.11g. Both WLANs may be using the same channels (channels 1, 6 and 11) and channel 1, for example, of one business could be overlapping the area of coverage of channel 1 of the other business.

Wi-Fi network devices using the 2.4GHz frequency typically have their channels set to channels 1, 6 and 11 by default. One of the ways to help identify and mitigate interference from other radio signals is to perform a wireless site survey or audit. This can be done through what's called a wardrive (or warwalk or warbike) using a hardware or software Wi-Fi spectrum analyzer tool, also referred to as a Wi-Fi stumbler, sniffer or surveyor.

Metal objects provide the highest amount of Wi-Fi interference from objects. Below is a list of other objects that can cause interference to Wi-Fi signals:

- **High interference:** Concrete, plaster and bulletproof glass.

- **Medium interference:** Bricks, water and marble.

- **Low interference:** Wood, glass and synthetic materials.

■ **Question:** What causes the highest amount of interference for wireless networks?
■ **Answer:** Metal objects provide the highest amount of Wi-Fi interference.

■ **Question:** What could be the problem when a person's Wi-Fi device works with one Wi-Fi network but not with another Wi-Fi network?

- **Answer:** The person's Wi-Fi device may be operating on one frequency only, such as 2.4GHz, and the Wi-Fi network that works with this device is also using 2.4GHz; but the other Wi-Fi network that does not work with that device is using 5GHz.

Note: 2.4GHz wireless devices are not compatible with 5GHz Wi-Fi networks, just as 5GHz wireless devices are not compatible with 2.4GHz Wi-Fi networks. If the Wi-Fi network uses dual band frequencies (2.4GHz and 5GHz simultaneously such as 802.11n or 802.11ac), then a wireless device using either 2.4GHz or 5GHz would work with that Wi-Fi network.

- **Question:** What do wireless networks use to prevent collisions on the network.
- **Answer:** Carrier Sense Multiple Access with Collision Avoidance (CSMA/CA).

Note: CSMA/CA is a layer 2 protocol used by nodes to avoid collisions by only transmitting signals when they sense the channel is idle. CSMA/CA will listen first before transmitting, and if the medium is already busy with transmissions occurring, CSMA/CA will wait until the medium is idle.

CSMA/CA is different from Carrier Sense Multiple Access with Collision Detection (CSMA/CD) in that, although CSMA/CD also listens first before transmitting, it continues operating after detecting the occurrence of collisions and terminates transmissions once collisions are detected. The nodes using CSMA/CD that sense the collision will wait for a certain amount of time before attempting to retransmit their signal. CSMA/CA is typically used in wireless networks while CSMA/CD is used in wired networks.

- **Question:** What tools can you use to check, troubleshoot or analyze signal strength, signal obstructions, Wi-Fi channels and other information about a Wi-Fi network?
- **Answer:** You can use one of many hardware or software Wi-Fi spectrum analyzer tools, also referred to as a Wi-Fi stumbler, sniffer or surveyor.

Note: One of the ways to help identify and mitigate interference from other radio signals, locate Wi-Fi dead spots or obstructions, or identify the best locations to mount access points is to perform a wireless site survey, audit or wardrive (or warwalk or warbike) using a hardware or software Wi-Fi spectrum analyzer tool, also referred to as a Wi-Fi stumbler, sniffer or surveyor. Many of these Wi-Fi stumblers or sniffers can be downloaded for free onto your laptop or you can buy handheld hardware versions that do the same thing.

WI-FI DEVICE COMPONENTS Q&A

- **Question:** What are the basic physical components that make up a wireless network?
- **Answer:** The are three basic components of a wireless network: (1) a wireless network interface controller/card (NIC) on the user's wireless device; (2) the wireless access point (AP); and (3) a wireless LAN access controller (WLC) referred to simply as controller.

Note: Most laptops, desktop computers, tablet and other wireless devices come with the wireless NIC (WNIC) built-in or a wireless NIC can be installed in some of these devices that don't have a built-in WNIC.

Access points (APs) are the interface between wireless devices and the wired network. There are two types of access points: autonomous AP and controller AP.

The autonomous AP, also known as fat AP or thick AP, are access points with built-in controllers. An autonomous AP is a standalone device commonly used in a home or small business. They are for small scale use where each autonomous AP device must be configured locally such as your home wireless router or when a small business, such as a coffee shop, has a small wireless network with perhaps only three autonomous APs to configure. An autonomous AP most of us are familiar with who use WiFi at home is the wireless router we get from our service provider. In addition to providing AP duties, this standalone device may also act as a router, switch, firewall and provide encryption.

For large wireless networks, the controller AP, also referred to as controller-based APs, uses a separate WLAN controller (WLC) server device to add, configure and control multiple APs called thin APs or lightweight APs (LAPs or LWAPs). In controller AP configurations, the WLAN controller acts as a switch for each AP-to-controller connection, and as a router for the controller-to-wired network connection.

The WLAN controller can be imbedded or modularized in a switch or router, or deployed in the form of a virtual WLC that runs on VMware ESX/ESXi. Depending on the vendor model, the WLC can also perform other functions besides switching and routing, such as encryption, authentication, and access control to certain applications (authorization); quality of service (QoS); network address translation (NAT); firewall, intrusion detection system (IDS) and intrusion prevention system (IPS); virtual private network (VPN) access; spectrum monitoring and analysis; and load balancing, power level and bandwidth management. Vendors also produce routers with WLC features built in.

There are now cloud-based controllers and controller-less APs. Cloud-based controllers help reduce expenses for companies who do not want to bother with costs associated with the purchase, operation and maintenance of controller devices.

Controller-less APs are simply thin APs that have their own virtualized controller within the AP. This eliminates the need for a separate WLAN controller device but still allows all thin APs in a large wireless network to be managed by one central interface without the expense of WLAN controller and a backup WLAN controller. Deploying only one WLAN controller creates a single point of failure for the entire wireless network. Controller-less APs eliminate the single point of failure and the extra expense of a second WLAN controller for high availability (HA).

In a small wireless network such as your home, the AP (wireless router) will connect to the service provider via a cable. In large wireless networks, each AP or lightweight AP (LAP) can connect, via a physical cable through a switch, to a WLAN controller as shown in Figure 5-5.

Figure 5-5 *Access Points (APs) communicating with a WLC*

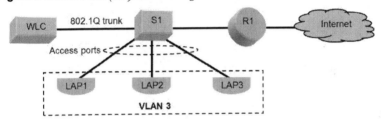

In the case of controller-less APs or a cloud-based controller, each lightweight AP connects to a switch in the company, hotel or wireless hotspot network. LAPs can also be interconnected in a mesh network through wireless connectivity where the physical location prohibits the use of cabling; however, this method reduces the bandwidth supported for each hop.

WI-FI ACCESS POINTS Q&A

■ **Question:** Assume a WLAN network infrastructure is in place and a new lightweight access point (AP) is installed in this WLAN network.

What is required for this AP to locate and connect to (join/register with) a wireless LAN controller (WLC) using the layer 3 mode?

- **Answer:** The following is required for the AP:

  - The AP will obtain its IP address and default gateway either through DHCP or statically configured.

  - The AP will send discovery request messages to locate all the available WLCs who respond with discovery respond messages that include their system name, AP-manager interface IP addresses, mode (layer 2 or layer 3 mode) and other pertinent information.

Note: APs communicate with WLCs using either the industry standard Control and Provisioning of Wireless Access Points (CAPWAP) protocol or the Cisco proprietary Light Weight Access Point Protocol (LWAPP).

WLCs will automatically respond to **discovery request** messages from APs without checking the validity of AP certificates or credentials. However, WLCs will not respond to **join requests** from APs until after the AP passes the certification or credentials check.

There can be more than one AP-manager interface on the WLC when link aggregation (LAG) is disabled, but it is recommended that only one AP-manager interface per WLC be used. Depending on the model, an AP-manager interface may handle as many as 48 APs.

- Once the AP builds a list of available WLCs, the AP will send a join request to one of the WLCs based on the AP's selection process. A join request requires the AP pass the certification or credentials check before the WLAN controller responds with a join reply message.

- Once the AP receives a join reply from a WLC, the AP will compare its own software image to the WLC's image. If the images are different, the AP will download the WLC's image and use it—this requires a reboot by the AP.

- Once the AP determines its image is the same as the WLC's image, the AP will download the configuration from the WLC and switches to the registered (join) state—this may initiate another reboot by the AP.

- Both the new AP and the WLC are now connected, communicating and ready to service wireless clients.

- **Question:** What is a Service Set ID (SSID)?
- **Answer:** The Service Set ID (SSID) is used to differentiate one Wireless LAN network from another WLAN network.

Note: All APs in the same WLAN network broadcast the same Service Set ID (SSID) to identify the name of the Wi-Fi network. This allows a mobile wireless device to roam (move) around and away from one AP's range to another AP's range within the same Wi-Fi network with uninterrupted access to that Wi-Fi's network connection.

A single WLAN controller can support multiple WLAN networks, each WLAN having their own unique SSID. The SSID uses a case-sensitive 32 alphanumeric ID that is in the packet headers of wireless communications between the AP and mobile wireless devices. You can also have multiple different SSIDs used on the same AP at the same time, each different SSID providing different access and security features to mobile devices. Typically only one SSID can be used on a wireless bridge. When a client wireless device sends out a probe looking for a WLAN network to connect to, each access point within the range of that client wireless device will respond back with a beacon containing the SSID of that access point. These beacons of different SSIDs sent back to your wireless device are displayed as a list of wireless networks you see on your mobile device when you are seeking to connect to a Wi-Fi network in your area. When multiple APs using the same SSID send back a beacon with the same SSID to your wireless device, your wireless device will select the beacon with the strongest signal and display that access point's SSID and signal strength on your wireless device.

Once you log into that AP with your wireless device, the AP will add the MAC address of your wireless device to its association table and begin providing your wireless device access to its Wi-Fi network.

Figure 5-6 shows two separate Wi-Fi networks in two adjacent buildings, each WLAN network using a different SSID (HotSpot1 and CoffeeHouse1).

Figure 5-6 *Different Service Set IDs (SSIDs) for separate WLAN networks*

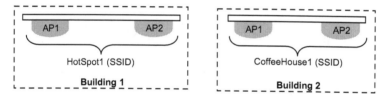

- **Question:** What 3 things are needed by a Wi-Fi device to connect as a guest to the wireless network at a business company?
- **Answer:** (1) A compatible 802.11 radio signal (such as 2.4GHz or 5Ghz) used between the Wi-Fi device and the AP; (2) the Service Set ID (SSID) used by the AP; and (3) the correct 802.1X/EAP credentials to access the Wi-Fi network.

Note: Both the Wi-Fi device and the AP must use the same frequency— such as 2.4GHz or 5GHz—in order for the Wi-Fi connection to work. If the Wi-Fi client device is using 2.4GHz and the Wi-Fi network uses 5GHz, a Wi-Fi connection cannot be established. All APs in the same WLAN network broadcast the same Service Set ID (SSID) to identify the name of the Wi-Fi network. A WLAN controller can support multiple WLAN networks, each WLAN having their own unique SSID.

IEEE 802.1X is a port-based network access control (PNAC) mechanism that takes the concept of authentication at the device level down to the ports/interfaces of devices. 802.1X can be used in wired and wireless networks and consists of three parts:

(1) **Supplicant**—the client device attempting to access the network.

(2) **Authenticator**—the network device such as the network switch or wireless access point (AP) which acts as a proxy between the client (supplicant), such as a mobile Wi-Fi device, requesting authentication from the authentication server.

(3) **Authentication server** such as an Internet Authentication Service (IAS) server—renamed Network Policy Server (NPS)—using Remote Authentication Dial-In User Service (RADIUS) and Extensible Authentication Protocol (EAP) that provide authentication, authorization and accounting (AAA) for network connections. 802.1X allows you to choose from several different authentication methods (over 40 different authentication methods) using EAP.

A commonly used EAP method in wireless networks is EAP-Transport Layer Security (EAP-TLS) that is a certificate-based authentication method that uses an authentication server. EAP-TLS is considered one of the strongest authentication and key determination methods.

■ **Question:** What are the management frames used to connect to an access point?

■ **Answer:** Discover, Authenticate and Associate.

■ **Question:** What does the Associate frame contain?

■ **Answer:** The Service Set ID (SSID), password, network mode (such as 802.11a/b/g/n/ac) and channel settings (such as 1, 6 and 11).

WIRELESS LAN CONTROLLER (WLC) Q&A

- **Question:** What does the wireless LAN controller (WLC) act like for connections to access points?
- **Answer:** A switch.

- **Question:** What does the wireless LAN controller (WLC) act like for connections to the wired network?
- **Answer:** A router.

- **Question:** What is the difference between the layer 2 and layer 3 modes on the wireless LAN controller (WLC)?
- **Answer:** The WLAN controller can operate in either layer 2 or layer 3 modes. In layer 2 mode, the lightweight access point (AP) and the WLC must be in the same subnet since they are not communicating using layer 3 IP addresses. In layer 3 mode, both the AP and WLC can be in different subnets because they both are using layer 3 routing for their IP addresses.

Note: When using layer 3 mode on WLAN controllers, APs can find the available WLCs through a variety of methods such as DHCP option 43 (and DHCP option 60); local broadcast by the WLC; manually configured; DNS; or the AP previously remembered the IP address of a specific WLC (known as priming).

DHCP uses configuration option codes numbering between 0 and 255. Option 43 of DHCP allows clients (including APs) to request vendor specific options—a private table of vendor proprietary information held separately by the DHCP server—by including a vendor string and vendor specific options (option 60) along with the option 43 request to the DHCP server. This allows the DHCP server to upload to the requesting client (the AP in our case) the proper configuration information for that specific vendor AP device. The vendor AP client device identifies itself (the type of vendor device it is) to the DHCP server using DHCP option 60.

- ■ **Question:** What is CAPWAP?
- ■ **Answer:** Control and Provisioning of Wireless Access Points (CAPWAP) is an IETF open standard protocol that allows a Wireless LAN controller (WLC) to communicate with and control multiple wireless termination points (WTP), also known as access points (APs) or lightweight access points (LAPs).

Note: RFC 5415 defined CAPWAP in 2009 to provide a non-Cisco proprietary communication protocol between WLCs and APs. The Cisco proprietary version of CAPWAP is Light Weight Access Point Protocol (LWAPP).

Over the years, CAPWAP became more popular than Cisco/Airspace proprietary LWAPP. Cisco has made a few changes to accommodate CAPWAP into their Cisco wireless devices. Cisco controller software releases prior to 5.0 support layer 2 or layer 3 LWAPP mode; Cisco controller software releases 5.0 and 5.1 support only layer 3 LWAPP mode; and Cisco controller software release 5.2 or later support only layer 3 CAPWAP mode.

CAPWAP supports only layer 3 mode on WLAN controllers, while Cisco proprietary LWAPP supports both layer 2 and layer 3 modes on the WLAN controllers.

CAPWAP uses UDP ports 5246 and 5347. LWAPP uses UDP ports 12222 and 12223. APs use CAPWAP (or LWAPP) to send discover request messages to locate the access controller (WLC). The controller uses CAPWAP (or LWAPP) to respond with a discover response message, at which time both the AP and controller will establish a secure connection using the Datagram Transport Layer Security (DTLS) protocol.

Figure 5-5 showed switch S1 providing interconnectivity between three lightweight access points (LAP1 to LAP3), a WLC and router R1 (for Internet access). The WLC is connected to an 802.1Q trunk port on switch S1. The LAPs are assigned to a VLAN and connect to access ports instead of trunks on switch S1 because APs do not understand VLAN tagging used in trunks.

■ **Question:** Can you explain the different types of interfaces on a WLAN controller (WLC)?

■ **Answer:** The WLC uses both physical and logical (virtual) interfaces. Following is an overview of the different types of interfaces on the WLC.

- **Console port interface:** This RJ45 physical interface is used to connect directly to the WLC out-of-band using a console cable to a management PC, just as with other network devices. There may also be a Mini USB Console port on the WLC, depending on the model.

- **Service-Port interface:** This RJ45 physical interface is used for out-of-band management of the WLC, such as a secondary console port connection.

Note: This port can also be used as a redundant port when there are two WLCs connected together for high availability (HA) deployments. Communication through this interface remains active during the WLC reboot process.

The Service-Port does not support VLAN trunking or tagging; therefore, this interface must be connected to an access port—not a trunk port—of a switch. Configuration of this Service-Port interface is optional.

The IP address used on the Service-Port interface must be in a different subnet (VLAN) than the AP-manager interface or other dynamic interfaces used for client/AP traffic. If you place the Service-Port in the same subnet (VLAN) as wired in-band client traffic or AP traffic (AP-Manager interface or management interface), you will not be able to access the management interface on the WLC.

The Service-Port, AP-Manager and Virtual interfaces are normally configured using the Startup Wizard. You can view and configure these interfaces and ports by going to **Controller > Interfaces** or **Controller > Ports** on the Cisco WLC web GUI or you can use CLI commands on the WLC. Some WLC models may not have some of these interfaces.

- **Distribution system interface:** This physical interface is used for in-band connection between the WLC and upstream devices in the wired network such as a switch.

Note: The Distribution system interface provides an in-band path for client and management traffic; and is the physical interface to reach logical interfaces on the WLC, such as the AP-Manager interface, management interface, Dynamic interface and redundant port interface.

Depending on the WLC model, the Distribution system ports can be four to eight RJ45 Ethernet ports or blank slots that accept small form-factor pluggables (SFPs) for copper or fiber connections. You can also aggregate multiple Distribution system interfaces into a single port, called a LAG group, using the 802.1AX (formerly 802.3ad) port standard. Only one LAG group is supported on the WLC. If Distribution system interfaces are aggregated, a switch must use EtherChannel to communicate with the WLC's aggregated link.

Since the WLC does not support industry standard Link Aggregation Control Protocol (LACP) or Cisco's proprietary Port Aggregation Protocol (PAgP), you must set the switch's EtherChannel mode to "on" which forces the switch's aggregated link into becoming an EtherChannel with the WLC's aggregated link. In other words, do not use the auto or desirable modes of PAgP or the passive or active modes of LACP on the switch. Configuration of this distribution system interface is required.

- **AP-Manager interface:** This logical interface is used for in-band layer 3 mode communication between APs and the WLC.

Note: An AP-manager interface is required if you are using layer 3 mode where APs can be on a different subnet than the WLC. You can have more than one AP-manager interface. A single AP-manager interface can handle many APs. The logical AP-Manager interface is reached in-band through the physical Distribution system interface.

For layer 2 mode, a management interface is required on the WLAN controller.

The WLC uses the IP address on the AP-Manager interface as the tunnel source for CAPWAP or LWAPP packets to APs; and the APs use the same IP address in their tunnel destination packets to the WLC.

- **Management interface:** This logical interface is the default interface used for in-band management of the WLC by management devices (the controller's web management GUI or SNMP) or for communication with servers (such as AAA, RADIUS or DHCP servers).

Note: Access points can talk with the WLC management interface when needed, such as with WLC models (WLC2504 and WLC5508) that do not have a dedicated AP-Manager interface. For layer 2 mode, a management interface is required on the WLAN controller.

The IP address on the management interface is the address you type in your management PC's web browser to log into the WLC to use the WLC web GUI. This management interface address is the only address you can ping on the WLC from another device. The logical management interface is reached in-band through the physical Distribution system interface. Configuration of this management interface is required.

- **Dynamic interface:** This logical interface is used in-band to link specific Service Set IDs (SSIDs) to specific VLANs in order to separate different wireless client traffic through VLANs (WLANs)—you cannot have two Dynamic interfaces on the same VLAN or IP subnet.

Note: Each WLAN SSID is mapped to its own separate logical Dynamic interface; and the Dynamic interface is mapped to a specific VLAN. This interface can also be used as a DHCP relay for its VLAN subnet. The logical Dynamic interface is reached in-band through the physical Distribution system interface.

You can assign one or multiple logical Dynamic interfaces to a physical Distribution system interface. Depending on the WLC model, you can configure up to 512 dynamic interfaces. Configuration of this dynamic interface is required.

- **Redundant port interface:** The logical redundant port uses one of the physical RJ45 Service Port interfaces on the WLC for high availability (HA) and failover when two WLCs are deployed and physically connected together using Ethernet cable.

Note: Primary (active) and secondary (standby-hot) WLCs in HA and failover configuration use these redundant ports to communicate role negotiations, configurations, synchronization and keepalive messages.

- **Virtual interface:** This logical interface is used by the WLC itself for services such as mobility management, VPN termination and guest web authentication (WebAuth).

Note: Although the virtual interface is used for communications between the WLC and Wi-Fi clients, the IP address used on the virtual interface is never in source or destination addresses of packets moving through the physical Distribution system interface.

This unique virtual interface IP address is used for all controllers within a mobility group for proper functioning of inter-controller roaming. Configuration of this virtual interface is required.

Mobility management includes controller roaming and DHCP relay for Wi-Fi clients who obtain their addresses from a DHCP server. WebAuth is used as the redirect address for the web authentication login page

- **Question:** What is an AP-manager interface?
- **Answer:** This logical interface is used for in-band communication between APs and the WLC. This interface is required if you are using layer 3 mode where APs can be on a different subnet than the WLC.

Note: Although you can have more than one AP-manager interface, only one AP-manager interface can be configured on a physical port. A single AP-manager interface can handle many APs. An AP-manager interface is required on a WLAN controller for layer 3 mode only.

There can be more than one AP-manager interface on the WLC when link aggregation (LAG) is disabled but it is recommended that only one AP-manager interface per WLC be used.

WI-FI SECURITY Q&A

- **Question:** What is the best type of encryption used for wireless networks?
- **Answer:** Wi-Fi Protected Access II (WPA2) encryption, also known as IEEE 802.11i.

Note: WPA2 uses Counter Mode Cipher Block Chaining Message Authentication Code Protocol (CCMP), an enhanced data cryptographic encapsulation mechanism based on 128-bit Advanced Encryption Standard (AES) encryption that replaced the weaker encryption of the Wired Equivalent Privacy (WEP) security protocol. CCMP provides authentication, confidentiality and access control for each wireless connection. In addition to using WPA2, a strong passphrase should also be used to provide another layer of security to the WLAN network.

WEP was initially used in 1997 to secure wireless networks but its 40-bit and 104-bit encryption keys proved too easy to break. In 2002, the Wi-Fi Alliance introduced Wi-Fi Protected Access (WPA) as an interim software-implementable solution to WEP until a more secure hardware solution (WPA2) was established in 2004 as the IEEE 802.11i standard (WPA was known as the draft IEEE 802.11i standard).

WPA software used only Temporal Key Integrity Protocol (TKIP) with a 128-bit encryption key that worked with legacy wireless hardware, but today, WPA is also considered no longer secure and is vulnerable to similar attacks as the WEP security protocol.

WPA2 can be used with two types of encryption: WPA2 with AES (WPA2-AES) or WPA2 with AES and TKIP (WPA2-AES/TKIP). More modern wireless clients will use AES; and older wireless clients may only use TKIP.

WI-FI MODES Q&A

- **Question:** What are the wireless modes?
- **Answer:** Ad-hoc mode which is a client to client mode such as between two wireless laptops, and Infrastructure mode. There are two types of Infrastructure modes: Basic Service Set (BSS) and Extended Service Set (ESS).

Note: The Basic Service Set (BSS) uses only one access point (AP). The wireless router your service provider provides you would be an example of the BSS mode.

The Extended Service Set (ESS) uses more than one AP as is commonly deployed in Wi-Fi hotspots and large businesses. With ESS, all of the APs using single band (WLANs using only 2.4GHz or only 5GHz, for example) broadcast the same Service Set ID (SSID) to identify the name of the Wi-Fi network; but each AP uses a different frequency channel (such as channels 1, 6 and 11 in 2.4GHz) to prevent interference between adjacent APs (interference occurs when adjacent APs are using the same frequency channel). Dual band Wi-Fi networks (WLANs using 2.4GHz and 5GHz simultaneously) will use a separate SSID for each of the 2.4GHz and 5GHz frequencies.

Figure 5-7 shows an indoor Wi-Fi network in ESS mode with four APs mounted to the ceiling, each AP using the same SSID (HotSpot1) but each AP is on a different frequency channel.

Figure 5-7 *Access Points (APs) with Extended Service Set (ESS) Infrastructure mode*

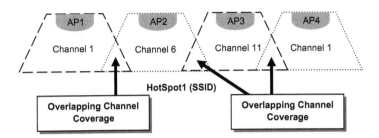

Although channel 6's radio coverage overlaps channels 1's and 11's radio coverage, no Wi-Fi interference will occur because each channel is on a different frequency spectrum that won't interrupt each other. Although both AP1 and AP4 use channel 1, their frequencies do not overlap each other because of their physical distance from each other's radio signal; therefore, their duplicate frequency channel will not produce interference.

SECTION SIX

The Last and Most Important Question

I wrote this book to give you help that will lead to success in your job search, particularly in the area of your IT job interview. It is my sincere desire that this book has blessed and encouraged you to that end.

I gain no greater satisfaction in life than to pass along to others the things I've learned to help others live a successful and prosperous life—not just in this life but the next. What do I mean by the *next life*?

- **The Last and Most Important Interview Question:** I'm not saying this will happen anytime soon, but if you were to die today, where would you go?

- **Same Question:** If God were to ask you why should He let you into heaven, what would you say?

- **Here's Your Answer:** The Bible says in Romans 3:23, *"We've all sinned and fallen short of God's glory."* Romans 6:23 says, *"The wages of sin is death and separation from God, but the free gift of God is eternal life and peace from God."* (see also Isaiah 59:2 and Romans 5:1) Romans 10:9 says, *"If you confess with your mouth the Lord Jesus and believe in your heart that God raised Jesus from the dead, you shall be saved."* Romans 10:13 says, *"Whoever calls on the name of the Lord Jesus shall be saved."*

Pray this quick prayer with me: *Heavenly Father, I believe Jesus died on the cross for me and my sins; and rose again from the dead. I give You my life. Lord Jesus, come into my heart and into my life. Amen.*

If you prayed that prayer, you are saved and going to heaven when you die because Jesus paid for all your sins—past, present and future sins. Now you know the answer to the most important interview question.

APPENDIX A

Terminal Settings

Following are terminal settings for terminal emulation software on your laptop/PC to connect to different vendor devices:

Cisco IOS and IOS-XE

- Speed (baud): 9600
- Data bits: 8
- Stop bit: 1
- Parity: None
- Flow control: None

Cisco IOS-XR

- Speed (baud): 9600
- Data bits: 8
- Stop bit: 2
- Parity: None
- Flow control: None

Cisco NEXUS NX-OS

- Speed (baud): 115200
- Data bits: 8
- Stop bit: 1
- Parity: None
- Flow control: None

Cisco 2921 term server

- Connection Type: Serial
- Serial Line: COM4
- Speed (baud): 9600
- Data bits: 8
- Stop bit: 1
- Parity: None
- Flow control: None

Telco: Same as Cisco's IOS settings

Juniper: Same as Cisco's IOS settings

Extreme: Same as Cisco's IOS settings

Alcatel-Lucent

- Speed (baud): 115200
- Data bits: 8
- Stop bit: 1
- Parity: None
- Flow control: None

Huawei

- Speed (baud): 38400
- Data bits: 8
- Stop bit: 1
- Parity: None
- Flow Control: None

MRV

- Speed (baud): 9600
- Data bits: 8
- Stop bit: 1
- Parity: None
- Flow Control: DSR/DTR

APPENDIX B

Satellite Communications (SATCOM) Terminology

Orbital Period: The orbital period is the time it takes for an object in space to complete one rotation or orbit around another object in space. There are different types of orbital periods, one of which is the sidereal time period or sidereal day.

Sidereal Day: One rotation of Earth's orbit—not its orbit around the sun but one rotation of Earth's axis—is measured in a sidereal day, and is roughly 23 hours, 56 minutes, 4.0916 seconds. Sidereal Time is the time scale system used to track the direction and speed of rotation of fixed objects, such as stars, in relation to Earth's rotational orbit. With this time-keeping system, an observer at any given point on Earth's surface can locate and identify a satellite in space at the same point in its orbit time scale—its sidereal time.

Geostationary Orbit (GSO): The orbit of an object, such as satellites, around Earth that is the same as the Earth's rotation. All geostationary satellites orbit at the same sidereal rotation path as Earth at about 22,236 miles (35,786 kilometers) directly above Earth's equator—a requirement to maintain geostationary orbit. Examples of geostationary satellites are weather, broadcast and communications satellites.

To keep things in perspective, the Hubble Space Telescope is 359.7 miles (595 kilometers) from Earth in an inclined (tilted 28.5 degrees) orbit above Earth's equator every 97 minutes; the International Space Station maintains an altitude from Earth between 205 miles (330 kilometers) and 270 miles (435 kilometers) while travelling 17,500 miles an hour to orbit Earth 15.5 times per day; and the moon is 238,900 miles (384,400 kilometers) from Earth, orbiting Earth once every 28 days (13 times per year).

The orbital period of geostationary satellites are equal to the sidereal rotational period of Earth—roughly 23 hours, 56 minutes, 4.0916 seconds for one complete rotation. From an observer on Earth's surface, the geostationary satellite appears stationary or fixed in the same spot in the sky. For this reason, satellite ground terminal antennas that track geostationary satellites, including your personal home satellite dishes, remain in a fixed position.

The average one-way latency of communications from a satellite ground terminal up to a geostationary satellite and back down to another satellite ground terminal is roughly 250 milliseconds (.25 seconds). The average round-trip latency of communications from a satellite ground terminal up to a geostationary satellite, back down to a second satellite ground terminal, and then back through the same satellite path to the first satellite terminal is roughly 500 milliseconds (0.5 seconds).

This additional inherent latency of network traffic using satellite communications causes havoc to network protocols such as TCP/IP and degradations in voice, video and data applications.

There are many vendor solutions to this problem, such as IP accelerators and WAN optimizers, to correct for satellite delay. WAN optimization is discussed in greater detail in *IT Questions and Answers For IT Job Interviews, Volume 4*.

Geostationary satellites can drift off course over time and must be corrected to maintain their designated orbit.

Geosynchronous Orbit (GEO): As with geostationary satellites, geosynchronous satellites move with Earth's sidereal rotation, but not in a fixed spot like GSO satellites. These GEO satellites repeat a curved pattern as they orbit in concert with Earth sidereal orbit—this pattern is called an analemma (from the Greek "pedestal of a sundial"). Examples of geosynchronous satellites are communications satellites.

From an observer on the earth's surface, the geosynchronous satellite appears to move repeatedly in the same figure eight pattern in the sky over the equator as it orbits Earth within the same sidereal day rotation path as Earth. For this reason, satellite ground terminal antennas that track geosynchronous satellites are constantly moving to keep track with the moving satellite.

The average one-way latency of communications from a satellite ground terminal up to a geosynchronous satellite and back down to another satellite ground terminal is the same as explained for GSO satellites.

Semi-Synchronous Orbit (SSO): Satellites in a semi-synchronous orbit are at a lower altitude from the earth than geosynchronous satellites. Global Positioning System (GPS) satellites are semi-synchronous satellites at an altitude of 12,613.8 miles (20,300 kilometers) from the earth and orbit Earth in 12 hours (two orbits per day).

Supersynchronous Orbit: Satellites in a supersynchronous orbit circle Earth in a longer sidereal period than Earth's own sidereal period. The moon is in a supersynchronous orbit when it orbits Earth. The moon orbits Earth once every 28 days (13 times per year) while Earth's sidereal orbit is 23 hours, 56 minutes, 4.0916 seconds. Space debris (decommissioned satellites) are another example of objects in a supersynchronous orbit.

Low Earth Orbit (LEO): Satellites in low Earth orbit have an altitude ranging from 99 miles (160 kilometers) to 1,200 miles (2,000 kilometers) from Earth, and travel around Earth at speeds of 17,000 miles an hour

(27,400 kilometers an hour) or more. At an altitude of 99 miles from Earth, it takes a LEO satellite only 1.5 hours to orbit Earth.

The circumference of Earth at the equator is roughly 24,902 miles (40,075 kilometers). So when you look up into the night's sky and see what appears to be a star moving steadily across the sky, chances are you are witnessing a LEO satellite orbiting Earth.

You could also be witnessing the International Space Station (ISS) that circles Earth 15.7 times per day at roughly 216 miles (348 kilometers) in altitude while traveling at speeds of 17,200 miles (27,700 kilometers) per hour. For those curious enough to want to catch a glimpse of the International Space Station at night, check out NASA's "Spot The Station" webpage at http://spotthestation.nasa.gov.

The Hubble Space Telescope is in low Earth orbit at 359.7 miles (595 kilometers) from Earth traveling 4.66 miles (8 kilometers) per second passing over Earth's equator every 97 minutes.

Inclined Orbit: The tilt or angle in degrees of a satellite's rotation as it orbits around Earth. The incline of the satellite's orbit need only be tilted at an angle other than zero degrees from the horizontal relation to the equator to be considered in an inclined orbit.

As mentioned earlier, the Hubble Space Telescope is in an inclined (tilted 28.5 degrees) orbit above Earth's equator.

Ascending Node: Only satellites in an inclined orbit have nodes. An ascending node is when an inclined orbit satellite is moving in its upward or northward ascending track of its orbit.

Descending Node: A descending node is when an inclined orbit satellite is moving in its downward or southward descending track of its orbit.

Ellipse Orbit: Some satellites orbit around Earth in an ellipse, oval or non-circular path. This means the satellite will be farther in altitude from Earth (apogee) at one point in its orbit, and then closer to Earth (perigee) at another point in its orbit around Earth.

Apogee: Some satellites orbit around Earth in an ellipse, oval or non-circular path. This means the satellite will be farther in altitude from Earth at one point in its orbit, and then closer to Earth at another point in its orbit around Earth. A satellite is in its apogee when its orbit around Earth is farthest in altitude from Earth. This is typically the satellite's slowest orbiting point around Earth.

Earth also circles the sun in an elliptical path in 365.25 days at an average speed of 67,000 miles per hour (30 kilometers per second)—it's farthest altitude from the sun (aphelion), in which it is at its slowest orbiting speed, occurs in early July at about 94.5 million miles (152 million kilometers) from the sun.

Perigee: A satellite is in its perigee when its ellipse orbit around Earth is closest in altitude from Earth. Earth also circles the sun in an elliptical path in 365.25 days at an average speed of 67,000 miles per hour (30 kilometers per second)—it's closest altitude from the sun (perihelion), in which it is at its fastest orbiting speed, occurs in early January at about 91 million miles (146 million kilometers) from the sun.

Major Axis: The major axis of a satellite in an elliptical (oval shaped) orbit is the longest point from the center of the circle to the edge of the circle of the satellite's orbit.

Minor Axis: The minor axis of a satellite in an elliptical (oval shaped) orbit is the shortest point from the center of the circle to the edge of the circle of the satellite's orbit.

Eccentricity: The orbital eccentricity of a satellite describes the amount at which a satellite deviates from a perfect circle when it is orbiting Earth. An eccentricity of zero is a perfect circle. Earth's eccentricity is roughly 0.0167 as it orbits the sun; the moon's eccentricity value is 0.0549 as it orbits Earth.

Disposal Orbit: Also known as the graveyard orbit or junk orbit, the disposal orbit is a supersynchronous orbit where space debris (decommissioned satellites that have reached the end of their operational life) are jettisoned or de-orbited into the graveyard orbit that is further in altitude than its operational altitude from Earth.

The Federal Communications Commission (FCC) has mandated that decommissioned satellites move 186.4 miles (300 kilometers) further in altitude from Earth. The European Telecommunications Standards Institute (ETSI) is the European equivalent to the FCC.

This disposal orbit is at a higher altitude from earth than geostationary and geosynchronous satellites to prevent any collisions with operational satellites and other operational space vehicles that could be possible within the earth's gravitational pull—particularly a collision scenario that would trigger what's called the Kessler effect.

The Kessler effect, also known as the Kessler syndrome, collisional cascading or ablation cascade, was a situation explained by the NASA scientist Donald Kessler in 1978. As Kessler explained it, a collision between two space vehicles such as satellites colliding could spread debris that would collide into other satellites, causing a cascade effect among the other satellites in space.

There are currently over 1,100 active and roughly 2,600 decommissioned satellites in space, and those numbers are growing, and traveling at high rates of speed such as the low Earth orbiting satellites that travel 99 miles to 1,200 miles from the earth at 17,000 miles an hour (27,400 kilometers an hour) or more.

If Kessler's collision scenario were to occur with the growing number of satellites in space, their debris could make low Earth orbits impassable, and the earth's gravitational pull could possibly draw some of this space debris into Earth's atmosphere.

Satellite Ground Tracks: The track line of a satellite's orbit that is projected onto Earth's surface to determine the satellite's orbital path. From an observer on the earth's surface, these ground tracks are points on Earth's surface where the satellite will pass directly overhead. These ground tracks can be plotted on a map to clearly see the orbital pattern of a particular satellite.

Ephemeris Data: Satellites transmit ephemeris data to provide timing, health status and information about its location at any given time. Satellite operators use ephemeris data to determine the operational health of satellites and to operate and maintain the satellite. Satellite ground terminal operators use ephemeris data to locate the satellite to properly point and align their satellite antennas at the satellite. People can use Global Positioning System (GPS) satellite ephemeris data to determine their current location on the ground or water, or provide directions to another location they want to reach.

Bird: A bird is just another name for a satellite.

Azimuth: The azimuth and elevation are the two measurements that allow you to properly point your satellite antenna in the direction of a satellite. The azimuth is the east-to-west horizontal direction you would point the satellite antenna. Elevation is the north-to-south vertical direction you would point the satellite antenna. These two coordinates will provide you the necessary vectors to aim the antenna directly at a particular satellite.

Look Angles: Satellite look angles are the azimuth and elevation readings to locate a particular satellite from your current location. Satellite look angles are also helpful seeing the line-of-site path from a satellite ground terminal or handheld device to the satellite in the sky, to determine if any objects are in your path such as buildings or trees that would block your view of the satellite.

Objects in the way of your line-of-site view of the satellite will degrade the signal communications between the satellite and the antenna of the satellite ground terminal or handheld device.

APPENDIX C

Satellite Frequency Allocations (Graphical)

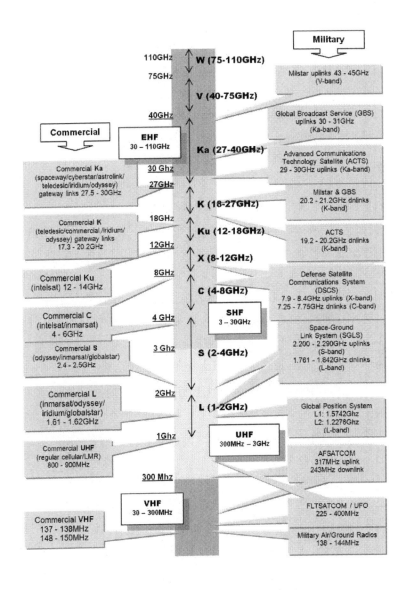

APPENDIX D

Rack Unit

Most private and public businesses and organizations keep their IT equipment stored in the same types of equipment cabinets, commonly referred to as racks. A rack unit, called "RU" or "U", is the industry unit of measure for determining how much space, in height, a piece of rack-mounted equipment will take up in one of these equipment racks. Figure D-1 provides an example of some rack units.

Figure D-1 *Rack unit measurements*

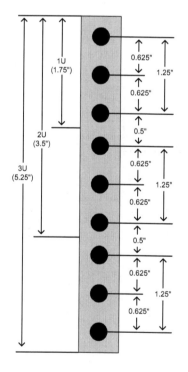

Rack Unit	Inches	Millimeters	Holes
1U	1.75	44.45	3
2U	3.5	88.9	6
3U	5.25	133.35	9
4U	7	177.8	12
5U	8.75	222.25	15
6U	10.5	266.7	18
7U	12.25	311.15	21
8U	14	355.6	24
9U	15.75	400.05	27
10U	17.5	444.5	30
11U	19.25	488.95	33
12U	21	533.4	36
13U	22.75	577.85	39
14U	24.5	622.3	42
15U	26.25	666.75	45
16U	28	711.2	48
17U	29.75	755.65	51
18U	31.5	800.1	54
19U	33.25	844.55	57
20U	35	889	60

One rack unit (1U) is equal to 1.75 inches (44.45mm) high, two rack units (2U) are equal to 3.5 inches (88.9mm) high, and so on. One rack unit (1U) includes three holes in the rack's vertical frame or 1.75 inches. The distance between three holes—first hole center to third hole center— equals 1.25 inches. Two rack units (2U) is 3.5 inches that include six holes, and so on. There is a 0.5 inch space between each three-hole group.

Equipment racks in government and commercial organizations come in different heights, from 3ft tall half racks (e.g. 18U or 22U racks) to 6ft tall racks (e.g. 42U or 44U racks), and these racks also come in varying widths and depths to meet the spacing and cooling requirements for vendor devices. Government racks containing equipment for classified data are usually marked with red indicators and are separated by the required distance from racks marked with black indicators containing equipment for unclassified data.

On both sides of the inside of these racks contain equipment mounting holes that are either threaded or unthreaded. The unthreaded holes require a threaded cage nut that clips on the hole.

There may be times when you have to measure rack space for projects such as auditing rack space; preparing for an upcoming installation of a single or multiple devices in a rack; or updating documentation showing rack space used or available for use. You can use a standard measuring tape to measure the distance between holes or the height of a device currently in the rack. However, there are measuring tapes designed specifically for measuring rack space. There are a variety of rack unit measuring tapes on the market that make it easy for you to determine the RU space a device may occupy or already occupies in an equipment rack.

APPENDIX E

Data Rate Chart

Data Rate Name	Data Rate	Number of 64Kbs Channels	Number of 1.544Mbs (T1)
DS0 (Data Service)	64 Kbps (8Kb overhead w/ AMI line code = 56Kbps)	1	0
T1 (Transmission Carrier)	1.544 Mbps (192Kb overhead per T1 w/ AMI line code = 1.352 Mbps; 8Kb overhead per 64Kbps)	24	1
DS1	1.544 Mbps	24	1
E1 (European Carrier)	2.048 Mbps	31	1
DS1C	3.1 Mbps	48	2
DS2	6.3 Mbps	96	4
E2	9.4 Mbps	145	6
Ethernet	10 Mbps	156	6
E3	34 Mbps	530	22
T3	44.7 Mbps	672	28
DS3	44.7 Mbps	672	28
OC-1 (Optical Carrier)	51.8 Mbps	810	33
Fast Ethernet	100 Mbps	1,562	60
DS4N4	139.2 Mbps	2,016	84
OC-3	155.5 Mbps	2,430	101
OC-9	466 Mbps	7,218	301
OC-12	622 Mbps	9,720	405
OC-18	933 Mbps	14,578	604
Gigabit Ethernet	1 Gbps (1000 Mbps)	15,625	647
OC-24	1.2 Gbps	18,750	777
OC-36	1.9 Gbps	29,678	1,230
OC-48	2.5 Gbps	38,875	1,619
OC-96	4.9 Gbps	77,750	3,293
OC-192	9.6 Gbps	150,000	6,217
10Gigabit Ethernet	10 Gbps (10,000 Mbps)	155,440	6,477
OC-256	13.271 Gbps	207,359	8,595
100Gigabit Ethernet	100 Gbps (100,000 Mbps)	1,554,480	64,770

APPENDIX F

Timing and Synchronization

The Beginning of Timing

Before we go over timing and synchronization, it's important to introduce a basic foundation for why we use the terms and metrics to describe some underlying concepts of timing and synchronization in today's networks and communications systems.

The frequency range of our human voice is roughly 200 hertz (Hz) to 4,000 hertz (4KHz). The Hertz (Hz) unit of measurement gets its name from German physicist Heinrich Rudolf Hertz who first proved the existence of electromagnetic waves. Today, Hertz is known as a unit of measure for frequency defined as one cycle per second.

When technology reached the point where it was now possible to convert analog signals, such as voice signals, to digital signals (a process called quantization), many people presented a sampling theorem to accomplish this conversion. Among these people were two Americans, electronic engineer Harry Nyquist and mathematician, electrical engineer and cryptographer Claude Shannon. Their theory is now known as the Nyquist-Shannon sampling theorem or simply the Nyquist theory.

Their theory stated that if you sample voice frequencies (200Hz–4KHz) at twice its highest frequent (8KHz—since the highest voice frequency is 4KHz), you would have enough samplings of the human voice to represent it in digital format of 1's and 0's. You could then transmit the digital signals to a receiver that could convert that digital representation back to a voice frequency that is intelligible to the human ear.

Over time, Nyquist's sampling rate has been incorporated into other advances in communications technology. For example, the Data Service 0 (DS0), which is 64Kbps, is the basic data rate in telecommunications from which all other data rates are described. 64Kbps is a multiple of Nyquist's 8KHz theorem (8,000 x 8 = 64,000); and each data rate such as T1, DS3, OC3, OC193, 10Gbps and 100Gbps are all multiples of 8,000.

In carrier communications systems, a frame is made up of 24 channels, and each channel is sampled 8 times (Nyquist's theorem) to properly represent voice transmitted on those channels.

The reason a frame in Time Division Multiplexing (TDM) is 193 bits is because 24 (channels) times 8 samplings (Nyquist's theorem) equals 192 bits; and then one frame bit is added to maintain synchronization between end-to-end communications equipment.

TDM, a commonly used multiplexing technique in communication systems, samples each channel successively from channel 1 to 24; and each of these sampled channels are placed in individual time slots one after the other. After 24 channels are sampled and placed into individual time slots, TDM will repeat this sampling again until the 24 channels are sampled a total of 8 times (again, this is Nyquist's theory). When all 24 channels are sampled 8 times and placed into time slots, and one synchronization bit is added to these samples, the resulting aggregate signal is a single 193 bit frame in TDM.

Although some companies or organizations may still be using TDM, it should be noted that the T1 data rate and TDM technology is legacy technology that can no longer keep pace with the increasing demands of voice, video and data requirements of networks in use today.

Nyquist's theorem translated over to the world's use of data bits today. Each bit of data uses multiples of the number 8. For example, in IT networks each byte of data is made up of 8 bits; and each octet in IPv4 addressing is 8 bits long.

Types of Timing

In the world of IT networks, Network Time Protocol (NTP) is a commonly used networking protocol for providing timing or clock synchronization between devices across networks. NTP uses a hierarchy, call a stratum, to identify timing sources, also known as reference clocks.

If a timing source (reference clock) is a device that originally produced the timing signal, it is identified as a stratum 0 timing source; and is considered the most accurate timing source in the hierarchy of timing sources. If a second network device receives its timing from a stratum 0 timing source, and then passes this timing to a third device, that second networking device is considered a stratum 1 timing source. If a third networking device (that received its timing signal from the second networking device) passes this timing signal to a fourth networking device, the third device is considered a stratum 2 timing source, and so on. Figure F-1 shows an example of how this NTP stratum timing source hierarchy may look in a network.

Figure F-1 *Stratum timing source hierarchy of NTP*

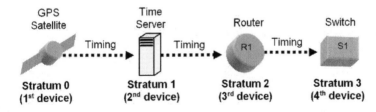

To view NTP timing source information on Cisco devices use the **show ntp [association | association detail | status]** commands.

The timing or clock sources used in networks and communications systems can be grouped in two categories: internal timing and external timing. Examples of internal timing sources are a device's internal clock, such as the internal clock on a time server, router or switch.

External timing sources are typically more accurate than internal timing sources. The following are examples of external timing sources:

- GPS satellite timing
- Stratum 0: Examples are atomic frequency (cesium or rubidium) clocks and GPS satellite clocks.
- Stratum 1: Network device clocks that received their timing from stratum 0 timing sources.
- Stratum 2: Network device clocks that received their timing from stratum 1 timing sources.
- Stratum 3: Network device clocks that received their timing from stratum 2 timing sources.

There are also protocols used to transport timing signals, such as Inter-range instrumentation group time codes (IRIG); WWV, the radio call sign of the United States National Institute of Standards and Technology (NIST) HF radio station that transmits timing signals; and DCF77, the radio call sign of the German radio station that transmits timing signals in Europe.

Frame Synchronization

In digital communications, frame synchronization or framing is used between end-to-end circuits on a carrier system to ensure the data sent by the transmitting equipment is correctly received by the receiving equipment. When voice, video and data communications are converted into data frames for transmission, such as in TDM systems, a fixed digital pattern of 1's and 0's called a framing bit is inserted at the starting time slot of each data frame. The framing bit is used to mark the start of valid frames of communications. This start bit also marks the end of the previous frame.

The receiving equipment will synchronize with this fixed framing bit pattern, called frame synchronization. The transmitter and receiver must use the same frame synchronization scheme in order for them to send and receive these frames of information successfully.

In carrier systems, one T1 frame is 193 bits. The 193-bit T1 frame comes from the fact that one T1 holds 24 DS0 channels of 64Kbps in each channel. Each 64Kbps DS0 channel carries 8 bits of sampled data (Nyquist's theory). After all 24 channels are sampled 8 times, one framing bit is added making a 193-bit T1 frame (24 DSO x 8 sampled bits = 192 bits + 1 framing bit = 193 bits in each T1 frame).

A Superframe is 12 T1 frames for a total of 288 channels. The pattern of 1's and 0's of each framing bit will be different for each of the channels in order to identify which 8 bits of sampled data belong to which channel on the receiving end.

An Extended Superframe (ESF) is 24 T1 frames for a total of 576 channels. ESF also includes Cyclic Redundancy Check (CRC) for error detection. The more complex ESF was developed to prevent the frame synchronization sequence from accidentally being produced by a test tone or other tones introduced in the communication line.

Line Code Synchronization

In digital communications, line coding helps maintain synchronization between end-to-end circuits on communications systems.

On a carrier system or other communications systems, information such as voice, video and data are converted to 1's and 0's before being transmitted to the distant end. 1's are sent by applying voltage (or the presence of light in optical equipment) on the line, and 0's are sent by applying the absence of voltage (or the absence of light in optical equipment) on the line.

Excessive zeros (excessive absence of voltage or light) in a row could cause receiving equipment to lose synchronization with sending equipment. Therefore, it is important not to send excessive zeros in a row to prevent loss of synchronization. This is accomplished through line coding techniques.

Both Alternate Mark Inversion (AMI) and Binary 8 with Zero Substitution (B8ZS) are line coding methods used in T1 carrier systems to prevent loss of synchronization between the receiving equipment and sending equipment.

AMI, the original standard of line coding, specifies that there are three states of the line:

(1) No voltage is a zero digit (or space)
(2) Positive voltage is a 1 digit (or mark)
(3) Negative voltage is also a 1 digit (or mark)

Because of the inversion of the voltage sinewave for each 1 digit (mark) sent, the receiving equipment can easily determine the data rate of the line and not lose synchronization.

B8ZS builds upon this older AMI method by using violations of the AMI rule to replace a pattern of eight zeros in a row. B8ZS does this by inserting (substituting) 1's after eight successive 0's. Thus, the name binary 8 with zero substitution (B8ZS).

AMI uses 8 Kbps of overhead for each 64 Kbps channel in a T1 to maintain synchronization leaving only 56 Kbps per channel in a T1. This 8 Kbps of overhead consumes a total of 192 Kbps of overhead for all 24 channels in a T1 circuit.

B8ZS, on the other hand, does not consume overhead bits from each channel like AMI because B8ZS uses bipolar violations to synchronize devices at both ends. Therefore, B8ZS provides the full T1 bandwidth for traffic. B8ZS is not compatible with AMI.

APPENDIX G

Types of Ethernet Cable

CABLE NAME	SPEED	ETHERNET TYPE	CABLE TYPE	IEEE	MAX CABLE LENGTH
Ethernet	10Mbps	10BaseT	CAT5, 5e, 6 (UTP)	802.3	100m (328ft) 100m (328ft)
Fast Ethernet	100Mbps	100BaseTX	CAT5, 5e, 6 (UTP)	802.3u	100m (328ft) 100m (328ft)
Gigabit Ethernet	1000Mbps (1Gbps)	1000BaseT	CAT5e (UTP) 6 (UTP or STP)	802.3ab	100m (328ft) 100m (328ft)
10Gigabit Ethernet	10000Mbps (10Gbps)	10GBaseT	Cat6 (UTP or STP)	802.3ae	55m (180ft)
10Gigabit Ethernet	10000Mbps (10Gbps)	10GBaseT	CAT6a (STP)	802.3ae	100m (328ft)
10Gigabit Ethernet	10000Mbps (10Gbps)	10GBaseT	CAT7 (STP or SCTP)	802.3ae	100m (328ft) 98m w/ SCTP
Gigabit Ethernet	1000Mbps (1Gbps)	1000BaseFX	Multimode fiber	802.3z	400m (1312.3ft) 62.5 micron
Gigabit Ethernet	1000Mbps (1Gbps)	1000BaseSX	Multimode fiber	802.3z	275m (853ft) for 62.5 micron / 550m (1804.5ft) for 50 micron
Gigabit Ethernet	1000Mbps (1Gbps)	1000BaseLX	Multimode fiber	802.3z	550m (1804.5ft) for 50 & 62.5 micron
10Gigabit Ethernet	10000Mbps (10Gbps)	10GBaseLX	singlemode fiber	802.3ae	10km (6.2mi) 9 micron

UTP is unshielded twisted pair 100-ohm grounded cable. STP is shielded twisted pair 150-ohm grounded cable. Screened twisted pair cable (SCTP or ScTP) is a hybrid of UTP and STP mostly used in Europe. SCTP is similar to STP cable but each twisted pair has no individual shield; it only uses an outer foil shield as in STP. Therefore, SCTP is also referred to as foil twisted pair (FTP). SCTP uses 100-ohm grounded cable. Improperly grounded cable can cause the shield in STP or SCTP to act like a transmitting and receiving antenna producing noise problems.

SCTP provides greater protection from RF interference than UTP and STP. Cat7 uses SCTP cable that provides the greatest protection from RF interference; however, it is not as popular in the US as in Europe.

Cat5e and Cat6 both have a maximum cable length of 100 meters (328 feet) for 10/100/1000 Mbps speeds. However, at 10 Gbps, the maximum cable length for Cat6 is 55 meters (180 feet). Therefore, Cat6a is recommended for 10 Gbps speed and above because its maximum cable length is 100 meters (328 feet) at 10 Gbps speed. Cat6a supports higher speeds (500Mhz) than both Cat5e (100Mhz) and Cat6 (250Mhz). Cat5e does not support 10 Gbps traffic.

Cat6 is backward compatible with Cat5 and Cat3. Both commercial enterprises and government organizations are continuously upgrading their Cat5 infrastructure with Cat6. Cat6 supports higher speeds (250 Mhz) with less crosstalk than Cat5e (100Mhz). Cat6 has lower crosstalk and less loss than Cat5 (54db versus 43db, respectively, of nearend crosstalk at 100Mhz). This translates to Cat6 having a better signal-to-noise ratio than Cat5 making Cat6 12 times less noisy than Cat5.

Cat6 has less crosstalk than Cat5e due to pairs of wires in Cat6 being insulated; something Cat5e does not have. Cat6a has less crosstalk than Cat6 because Cat6a is considerably thicker than Cat6 due to thicker insulation around each individual wire and tighter winding of each pair of wires.

The better signal-to-noise ratio at higher bandwidth of Cat6 (250Mhz) and Cat6a (500Mhz) over the Cat5 maximum bandwidth (100Mhz) makes Cat6 and Cat6a more reliable (fewer errors) for current applications and able to handle higher data rates for future applications.

Multimode fiber has a larger core diameter (50 or 62.5 micron) than the 9 micron core of singlemode fiber, allowing multiple wavelengths (lambda) of light to pass through multimode fiber versus only a single wavelength of light that can pass through singlemode.

Data rates in fiber cabling is inversely proportional to distance. In other words, the higher the data rate in fiber, the shorter the distance data can travel through fiber cabling.

The light or wavelengths of light used in fiber cables is measured in nanometers (nm). A nanometer is one-billionth of a meter, and is used as a unit of measure for things that are very small such as atoms, molecules and wavelengths of light beams.

Fiber cables can use either the older light emitting diode (LED) or laser light sources. There are three primary wavelengths of light for fiber optics: 850, 1300 and 1550 nanometers (nm). These three wavelengths are chosen because the attenuation produced by the absorption and scattering effects of the light within fiber cable is much less at those wavelengths. The US National Institute of Standards and Technology (NIST) use these three wavelengths in their power meter calibrations for fiber optics. Therefore, manufacturers use these same wavelengths in their design and testing of fiber optics.

LED light, typically 850 or 1300 nm, produces a lower power source than laser light that typically uses 1310 or 1550 nm. 850 nm LEDs were prevalent in devices in the 1980s and 1990s. Therefore, the larger diameter 62.5 micron fiber was originally deployed in commercial and government network infrastructures instead of the smaller diameter 50 micron fiber because of the greater power budget when using the wider diameter 62.5 micron fiber with LEDs.

Multimode cable can use either 850 or 1300 nm laser light, and typically uses 1300 nm for multimode fiber. Singlemode fiber typically uses either 1310 or 1550 nm laser light.

Today, 62.5/125 micron multimode fiber (125 represents the diameter of the cladding surrounding the 62.5 micron fiber core) is still commonly used in many fiber network infrastructures such as at the desktop and for adding segments to your existing network.

As bandwidth, speed and distance requirements continue to increase, more organizations are leaning toward using 50 micron multimode fiber to fill their backbone requirements. Although 50 micron fiber has a smaller core than 62.5 micron fiber, 50 micron multimode fiber provides three times more bandwidth than 62.5 micron fiber—500Mhz-km at up to 550m (1804.5 feet) versus 160Mhz-km at up to 220m (721.8 feet), respectively.

Thus, 50/125 fiber can be used as a fiber backbone at inter-building or intra-building connections for higher bandwidth needs (10Gbps) at higher speeds over longer distances than 62.5 micron can support.

The singlemode 9 micron fiber cable also handles bandwidth up to 10 Gbps and is typically used for very long distances (long-haul) up to 10km (6.2 miles).

Duplex fiber cable contains a pair of fiber strands that allow simultaneous bi-directional data transfer for devices such as fiber switches and servers, fiber modems and workstations.

Simplex fiber cable contains single fiber strands for either transmitting data or receiving data one-way but not both directions at the same time. Either duplex or simplex fiber strands can be used with multimode or singlemode fiber cables.

Although you can connect both 50 micron and 62.5 micron fiber cables to devices, such as a switch, router or server, it is not advisable to connect 50 micron fiber directly to 62.5 micron fiber because this will create an excessive loss of power when light of the larger 62.5 micron fiber tries to fit in the smaller diameter core of the 50 micron fiber cable.

APPENDIX H

Types of Ethernet Cable Connector Pinouts

Switches, hubs and repeaters must use straight-through cables to connect to a PC, router, server, wireless access point (AP), or network printer. Switches, hubs, and repeaters must use crossover cables to connect to another switch, hub or repeater. A PC, router, server, wireless AP or network printer must use crossover cables to connect to another PC, router, server, wireless AP or network printer. Also, a router uses a straight-thru cable to connect to a cable modem.

You can configure the interface to accept either straight-through or crossover cables regardless of the device match. Hubs and switches send data on pins 3 and 6 and receive data on pins 1 and 2 shown in Figure H-1. Ethernet NICs of a PC/router/server/wireless AP/network printer send data on pins 1 and 2 and receive data on pins 3 and 6. RJ-45 cables have 8-pin connectors on each end. Devices with speeds up to Fast Ethernet (100Mbps) use only pins 1 and 2 and pins 3 and 6. Devices with Gigabit Ethernet (1000Mbps) use pins 1 thru 8.

Figure H-1 *Straight-through Ethernet cable pinouts for RJ-45 connectors for T568B cabling (10Base-T, 100Base-TX, and 1000Base-T)*

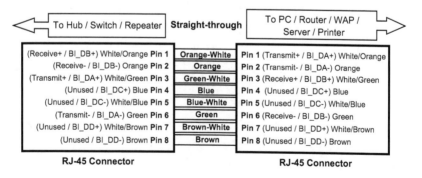

198

A crossover cable is needed whenever you connect like devices. In other words, you need a crossover cable instead of a straight-through cable whenever you connect a PC, router, access point (AP) or server to another PC, router, access point (AP) or server. At the same token, you must use a crossover cable instead of a straight-through cable whenever you connect a hub, switch or repeater to another hub, switch or repeater. Figure H-2 shows the crossover cable.

Figure H-2 *Crossover cable pinouts for RJ-45 connectors for T568B cabling (1000Base-T)*

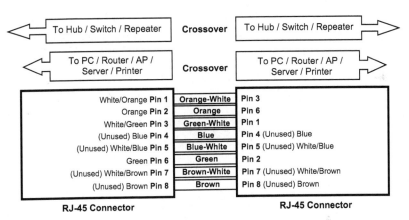

A console (rolled) cable is required between the console port of a device (switch, router, server, etc.) and a PC as shown in Figure H-3. An RJ-45 to DB-9 adapter can be used for PCs or dumb terminals requiring a DB-9 connection. Simply attach the RJ-45 jack end of the RJ-45 to DB-9 adapter to the end of the RJ-45 connector on the device. For laptops that use USB ports, you may need a USB male to RJ-45 adapter.

Figure H-3 *Console (rollover) cable pinouts for RJ-45 connectors for T568B cabling*

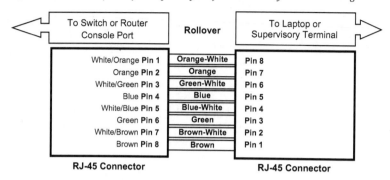

IEEE 802.3af describes power over Ethernet (PoE) as using a standard straight-through Ethernet cable to supply power, such as 48 volts of DC (VDC) at 15.5 watts across the same unshielded twisted-pair wiring as data of the Ethernet cable, called Alternative A. Pins 1 and 2 are used for positive voltage; and pins 3 and 6 are used for negative voltage for Alternative A. Alternative B places the power and data on separate pairs of wires; utilizing pins 4, 5, 7 and 8 for this purpose.

IEEE 802.3at provides 48 VDC at up to 50 watts across the Ethernet cable. This additional wattage of power allows PoE to power other devices that require more power than the 15.5 watts provided by 802.3af. Figure H-4 shows the pinouts used for IEEE 802.3af and 802.3at for PoE.

Figure H-4 *Power over Ethernet (PoE) cable pinouts for RJ-45 connectors for T568B cabling (10Base-T, 100Base-TX, and 1000Base-T)*

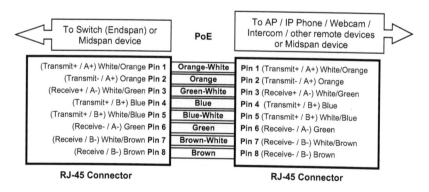

APPENDIX I

Troubleshooting with RS-530 Patch Panel Loopbacks

Many organizations, particularly government and military agencies, have classified and unclassified networks. Classified networks are called the "red" side; and unclassified networks are called the "black" side. Both the red and black side networks included red and black side devices, cabling, racks, infrastructure and patch panels.

Patch panels are not only used to physically interconnect circuits; they are used to troubleshoot circuits. Figure I-1 shows the EIA-530 K-patch panel consists of three jacks: the equipment (E) jack; line (L) jack; and monitor (M) jack.

Figure I-1 *Vertical RS-530 patch panels shown with RS-530 loopback plug*

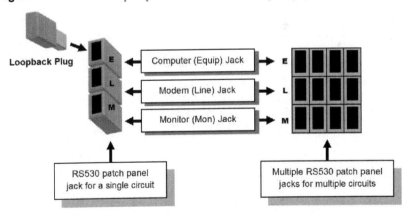

The equipment jack faces in the direction of equipment, such as computers, on the local LAN. The line jack faces in the direction of the external line where the modem is located. The monitor jack allows you to monitor the traffic flowing through the K-patch panel without interrupting the traffic.

The EIA-530 K-patch panel can be installed vertically or horizontally in equipment racks. Figure I-2 shows a single EIA-530 K-patch panel installed in a horizontal position. EIA-530 K-patch panels are commonly stacked in a horizontal position as shown at the bottom of Figure I-2.

Figure I-2 *Horizontal RS-530 patch panels*

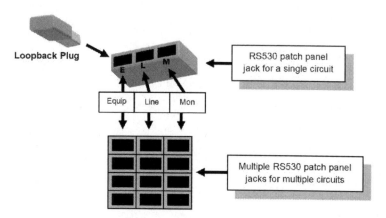

The K-patch panel can have a red (classified unencrypted) and black (unclassified encrypted) side that are kept separate from each other by cryptographic (crypto) devices that encrypt and decrypt the traffic flowing between the red side K-patch panel (into the classified side of the network) and the black side K-patch panel (into the unclassified side of the network). Figure I-3 shows a red side EIA-530 patch panel and black side EIA-530 patch panel separated by a crypto device.

Figure I-3 *Horizontal RS-530 patch panels with loopbacks in two directions (local and remote)*

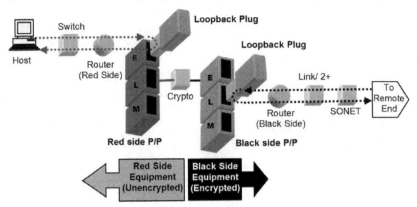

You can emplace loopbacks in different directions on the EIA-530 patch panel, such as the local loopback (also referred to as local-to-local loopback) or remote loopback (also referred to as local-to-remote loopback), by using loopback plugs.

Red side local loopbacks on the equipment (E) jack of K-patch panels, such as the EIA-530 patch panel, do not include crypto devices within the loop as shown in Figure I-3. This type of local loopback will loop traffic from the internal LAN network back to itself; and will block and bring down traffic from the remote end. However, the crypto timing will pass through the red side K-patch loop to the router on the red side. K-patch local loops on the red side are bi-directional.

Black side remote loopbacks on the line (L) jack of EIA-530 patch panels do not include crypto devices within the loop as shown in Figure I-3. This type of remote loopback will loop traffic from the remote location back toward the remote location; and will block and bring down traffic on the local LAN. K-patch loops on the black side are bi-directional.

You can also perform a local-to-local loopback on the black side of the EIA-530 patch panel as shown in Figure I-4. This loop emplaces an EIA-530 loopback plug on the equipment (E) jack of the black side EIA-530 patch panel. This allows you to verify that all the equipment, including the crypto device, and traffic on the red side (classified unencrypted) network is functioning properly. This loopback will cut off traffic from the remote end; resulting in the remote end traffic going down.

Figure I-4 *Horizontal RS-530 patch panels with local-to-local loopback on black side patch panel*

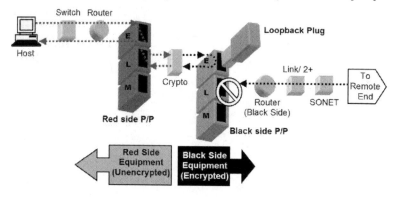

Figure I-5 shows an example of a local-to-remote loopback on the red side patch panel using an EIA-530 loopback plug.

Figure I-5 *Horizontal RS-530 patch panels with local-to-remote loopback on the red side patch panel*

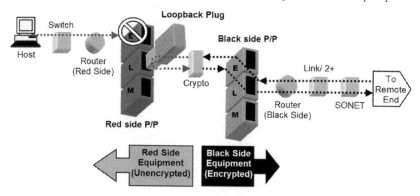

This loop emplaces a loopback plug on the line (L) jack of the red side EIA-530 patch panel. This allows you to verify that the crypto device and all equipment and traffic on the black side (unclassified encrypted) network is functioning properly. This loopback will cut off traffic from the local end; resulting in the local end traffic going down.

You can also monitor traffic in a non-intrusive manner or monitor and test traffic intrusively. Monitoring traffic in a non-intrusive manner means you do not interrupt the traffic during monitoring. You would use the monitor (M) jack on either the red side or black side EIA-530 patch panel for this purpose. You can also perform intrusive testing or monitoring of traffic.

Figure I-6 shows a piece of test equipment that is inserted into the monitor (M) jack of the red side EIA-530 patch panel. This allows you to test or monitor the bi-directional traffic at this point of the end-to-end path in a non-intrusive manner. This test will nether interrupt nor cut off traffic at either the local or remote ends.

Figure I-6 *Horizontal RS-530 patch panels with intrusive testing*

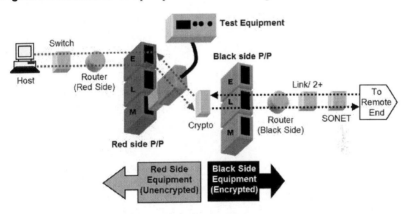

Figure I-7 shows a piece of test equipment that is inserted into the line (L) jack of the red side EIA-530 patch panel. This allows you to intrusively test or monitor the crypto device and the path and traffic through the crypto device to/from the remote end. However, this test cuts off traffic at the local end.

Figure I-7 *Horizontal RS-530 patch panels with intrusive testing*

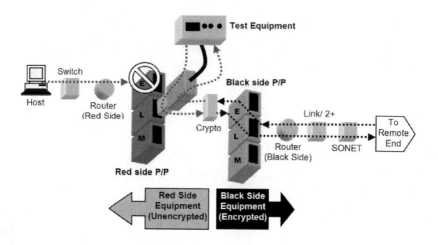

APPENDIX J

Troubleshooting with DSX Patch Panel Loopbacks

DSX-1 patch panels are for T1 (1.544 Mbps) circuits. DSX-3 patch panels are for DS3 (44.7 Mbps) circuits. A DS3 is equivalent to 28 T1's. Since loopbacks on DSX-1 and DSX-3 patch panels are not bi-directional, two DSX-1 patch panels are sometimes placed back-to-back (using cross connect wiring), with one DSX-1 facing the user end equipment and the other DSX-1 facing the network (Line/distant) end as shown in Figure J-1. The following drawing shows two DSX-1 patch panels connected back-to-back (via cross-connect wiring) with loopback plugs causing loops to both the local user end and the network (line/distant) end.

Figure J-1 *DSX patch panels shown with DSX loopbacks in both directions*

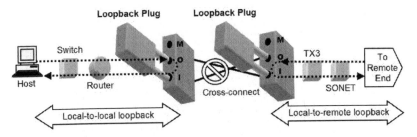

The DSX patch panel has an In (I) jack, Out (O) jack and a monitor (M) jack as shown in Figure J-2. The In jack faces in the direction of equipment, such as computers, on the local LAN. The Out jack faces in the direction of the external line where the modem is located. The monitor jack allows you to monitor the traffic flowing through the DSX patch panel without interrupting the traffic.

Figure J-2 *DSX patch panels shown with DSX loopback plug*

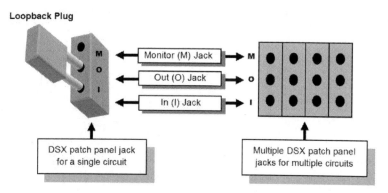

Figure J-3 shows where you should insert a test signal and where to read a signal on a DSX-1 patch panel when using test equipment. The Receive (RX) input on your T1 Test Set should connect to the "O" (Out) on the DSX-1 patch panel. The Transmit (TX) output on your T1 Test Set should connect to the "I" (In) on the DSX-1 patch panel.

Figure J-3 *Test set inserted in the DSX patch panel jacks*

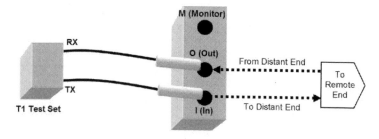

The Out (O) jack on the WAN-facing DSX patch panel is cross-connected to the In (I) jack on the LAN-facing DSX patch panel. The In (I) jack on the WAN-facing DSX patch panel is cross-connected to the Out (O) jack on the LAN-facing DSX patch panel.

When inserting test equipment into the In (I) and Out (O) jacks of the WAN-facing DSX patch panel, you are testing only from that DSX patch panel back across the WAN to the remote end as shown in Figure J-4. The local LAN side traffic is cut off. When inserting test equipment into the In (I) and Out (O) jacks of the LAN-facing DSX patch panel, you are testing only from that DSX patch panel back to the local LAN network. The traffic across the WAN from the remote end is cut off.

Figure J-4 *Test equipment on WAN-facing DSX patch panel jacks testing remote end traffic*

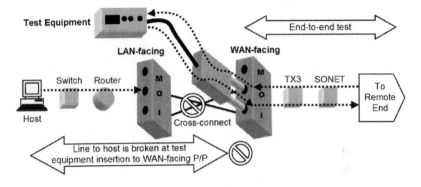

APPENDIX K

Troubleshooting Scenarios with Patch Panel Loopbacks

Troubleshooting with patch panels is commonplace in many patch and test facilities in both government and commercial enterprises. The following scenarios are a small sample of how patch panels are involved in the troubleshooting process to isolate the location of problems across networks. Refer to the drawings of patch panel loopbacks in the previous Appendixes as you review this section.

Problem scenario: Both ends up in loopbacks; down when normalized

This is a scenario where a government classified network circuit comes up when both ends perform all loopbacks on their patch panels, but the circuit goes down when loopbacks are removed and the circuit is normaled up.

Solution:

Have both ends check their encryption (crypto) devices for the following:

- Both crypto devices are using the same keying material (KEYMAT).
- Have both ends reload their crypto devices.
- Crypto settings are accurate at both ends.
- Check connections to crypto devices to ensure the Plain Text and Cipher Text cables were not reversed.
- Lastly, consider a possible inverse patch cable (tip-ring reversal or reversed pairs of wires).

Problem scenario: Can't see loopbacks from the router interface

- No loops were seen on the router interface of the local LAN after loopbacks were placed on the Red side or Black side K-patch panels or at other locations in-house at the local patch and test facility.
- The router interface at the local site was reset but still no loops are seen on the router interface.
- The cable between the router and the patch panel at the local site was checked and is good; but still no loop is seen on the router interface when a loopback is emplaced on the patch panel toward the router.
- Encapsulation is properly set to HDSL on the Cisco router.

Solution:

- Have the patch and test facility place a Fireberd test set on the red side patch panel jack facing the line (WAN) side or distant end. This would be the line (L) jack on a red side K-patch panel. This insertion point of the Fireberd test set into the red side patch panel includes the crypto device. This test will ensure the path from the red side patch panel to the black side patch panel is good; the crypto device is good; and the path across the WAN toward the remote end is good.
- Place a local loop somewhere after the crypto device on the line (WAN) side of the black side patch panel to loop the signal from the Fireberd test set back to itself.

  Bump (initiate) the crypto device after emplacing the loop. This will force the crypto device to sync up to itself.
- Have the patch and test facility perform a BERT test (using the Fireberd) through the loop to see if the crypto device will lock in sync to itself; and data is successfully passing through the loop as shown on the Fireberd test set.

- If the patch and test facility sees the crypto device lock in sync; and data is passing through the loop; have the patch and test facility continue extending the loopback out further away from the router toward the distant end (with the Fireberd still in place at the red side patch panel jack).
- Continue this procedure until the Fireberd no longer shows a good loop. When this test fails at a particular loop, check the network at the point of failure. If this loopback test shows the circuit good throughout each loopback, the router interface at the local end could be bad.
- Try swapping interfaces on the router at the local end; then recheck the router interface.

Problem scenario: Can't see loopback from router interface

- The router interface shows down/down.
- The router can't see any loops at all loopback locations.
- Both ends can place a Fireberd test set on the circuit, with a loopback at any location, and the data is passing successfully through each loop.
- No control signals (i.e. RTS/DTR/DCD/DSR) on the router interface.
- No 5-minute input or 5-minute output activity on the router interface.

Solution:

- Check for a loose or unattached cable on the router.
- Check the controllers cbus in the router using the **show controllers** or **show controllers cbus** command. If the cable to the router interface is unattached, the output of these commands will state: "No DTE cable" or "CABLE IS UNATACHED", respectively.

213

■   Have the patch and test facility reseat the router's cabling connectors (e.g. between router and K-patch panel or between router and ATM switch).

APPENDIX L

Troubleshooting with SONET Loopbacks

A Synchronous Optical Networking (SONET) multiplexer (mux) can receive several digital or optical inputs and produce an aggregate optical output such as an OC-12, OC-48, or OC-192; in addition to demultiplexing the aggregate signal back to the original individual signals in the output. Some examples of SONET mux's are the Cisco 15454 and the Alcatel 1603/12.

A common network topology that SONET multiplexers are configured in is the SONET ring where a group of SONET mux's are connected within a ring topology. When troubleshooting across SONET rings, you may not be the one who has access to the SONET devices. Therefore, you will have to contact the organization or agency that controls these devices to perform loopbacks for you so you can check your equipment through the loop and perform ping tests through the loop to check for continuity.

Oftentimes the name given to identify the "direction of a loopback" is defined by the controlling organization or agency. For example, suppose you are troubleshooting a network issue that uses SONET mux's in a SONET ring topology; however, the SONET devices at your local site and remote sites are controlled by another organization or agency. If you wanted the SONET controller—the person who remotely controls and implements loopbacks on the SONET device—to give you a "LOCAL to LOCAL loop" on your local SONET device (a loop on your local end SONET device facing toward your local enterprise equipment), you would ask for a "facility loop" as shown in Figure L-1.

This type of local loopback will loop traffic from your internal local LAN network back to itself through your local SONET mux; and will block and bring down traffic from the remote end. This allows you to verify that all the equipment on your local network up to the SONET mux is functioning properly.

Figure L-1 *Local SONET device in LOCAL to LOCAL loop (facility loop)*

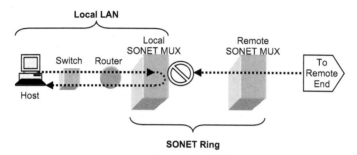

On the other hand, if you wanted a "REMOTE to LOCAL loop" (a loop on the directly connected distant ends SONET device facing your local site, you would ask for a "remote loop" on the distant end's SONET device as shown in Figure L-2.

This type of loopback will loop traffic from your local network back to itself across the SONET ring through the loop at the remote SONET device; and will block and bring down traffic from the remote end. This allows you to verify that all the equipment across the SONET ring and your local network is functioning properly.

Figure L-2 *REMOTE to LOCAL loop (remote loop) across a SONET ring*

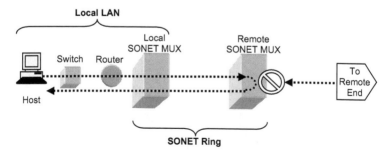

If you wanted a "LOCAL to REMOTE loop" on your local SONET device (a loop on your local end SONET device facing toward the distant end), you would ask for a "remote loop" on your local SONET mux as shown in Figure L-3.

This type of loopback will loop traffic from the external remote network back to itself through the loop at your local SONET device; and will block and bring down traffic at your local end. This allows you to verify that all the equipment across the SONET ring and the remote network is functioning properly.

Figure L-3 *LOCAL to REMOTE loop (remote loop) across a SONET ring*

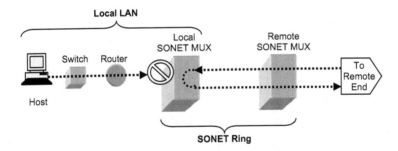

As you can see, the name of a loop may not be what its name might imply. So once again, it is always important to have the person performing the SONET loop for you to explain to you where exactly is the loop being placed and in what direction the loop is facing.

APPENDIX M

Troubleshooting with Promina (IDNX) Loopbacks

IDNX and Promina

Both the Integrated Digital Network Exchange (IDNX) and Promina were created by Network Equipment Technologies (N.E.T.). IDNX came on the scene before the Promina which replaced the IDNX as the next-generation multiplexer. However, you may still see and hear both names and devices used in different organizations and agencies.

The Promina and IDNX are considered an integrated packet/circuit switch that multiplexes inputs from digital data and analog (voice and video via the D-4 Channel Bank) and converts them into an aggregate T1 (1.544Mbps) or E1 (2.048Mbps) digital signal output. In addition to performing multiplexing operations, the Promina supports TDM, IP, frame relay, ISDN and ATM transport technologies. The Promina also performs automatic rerouting, QoS and bandwidth-on-demand (BoD) across the Promina network.

Hardware and software Promina loops are made at the same location on the Promina—on the Front Card, also known as the HSD card. A toggle switch on the Front Card creates a local hardware loop. Moving the switch to the "In" position means local loop; move the switch to the "Out" position means remote loop.

Timing will always pass through a Promina loop. Placing a loop (local or remote) on the Promina does not cut off timing. Therefore, you can see the loop from another device, such as a router or switch, that is part of the loop. Only the signal (voice, video, data) is cut off during the Promina loop when the signal is outside the loop.

The Promina receives only digital inputs; therefore, a Channel Bank is required to covert analog (voice and video) signals to digital format for input to the Promina.

D-4 Channel Bank

Traditional Channel Banks convert voice inputs to digital format. More sophisticated Channel Banks such as the ADNX-48 accept voice and digital data inputs and covert them to digital for the Promina or IDNX.

There are various types of Channel Banks ranging from D-1 through D-4. We will use the D-4 to continue our discussion of the channel bank. The D-4 version requires a DS-1 (64Kbps) input signal. The D-4 Channel Bank is made up of 24 channel modules; one power supply; and one Line Interface Unit. Each 64Kbps voice channel within the Channel Bank has its own module which provides a wide variety of services such as 4-wire and 2-wire E&M signaling.

The D-4 Channel Bank scans the individual channels in sequential order and time division multiplexes (TDM) these sampled channels into one aggregate output. The output is transmitted in blocks. These blocks are called Frames. Each Frame is made up of one 8-bit word from each channel followed by a single framing bit that is fed into the Promina or IDNX.

As with the SONET multiplexer, you may or may not be in control of the Promina multiplexer when troubleshooting across the Promina network. When you are troubleshooting across a Promina network, it's important to know where you can emplace loopbacks on the Promina in order to check the operation of equipment and the network, and perform ping tests through those loopbacks.

If you want the Promina controller—the person who remotely controls and implements loopbacks on the Promina mux—to give you a "LOCAL to LOCAL loop" on your local Promina device (a loop on your local end Promina device facing toward your local enterprise equipment), you would ask for either a "local hardware loop" or "local software loop" as shown in Figure M-1.

This type of local loopback will loop traffic from your internal local LAN network back to itself through the local Promina; and will block and bring down traffic from the remote end. This allows you to verify that all the equipment on your local network is functioning properly through your local Promina.

Figure M-1 *Local Promina (IDNX) loopback (hardware or software)*

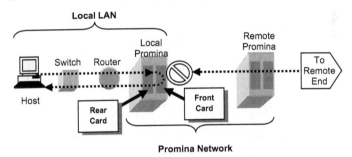

If you wanted a "REMOTE to LOCAL loop" (a loop on the directly connected distant end Promina device facing your local site, you would ask for a "remote loop" on the distant end's Promina device as shown in Figure M-2.

This type of loopback will loop traffic from your local network back to itself through the loop at the remote Promina device; and will block and bring down traffic from the remote end. This allows you to verify that all the equipment across the Promina network and your local network is functioning properly.

Figure M-2 *Local Promina (IDNX) loopback (hardware or software)*

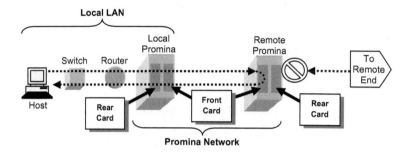

APPENDIX N

Troubleshooting with Timeplex Link/2+ Loopbacks

The Timeplex Link/2+ is an older multiplexer that provides full and half-duplex, first-level Time Division Multiplexing (TDM) that accepts up to two 18-slot chassis (one chassis nested above the other) of analog (voice and video) and digital data inputs; and converts them to up to 12 aggregate output trunks, each with speeds ranging from 4.8 Kbps to 2.048 Mbps (E1, not to exceed 7 T1's).

The Timeplex Link/2+ is oftentimes placed in tandem with the Timeplex TX-3 The Timeplex Link/2+, acting as the first-level mux, is placed closer to the local user equipment and the Timeplex TX-3, acting as the second-level mux, is located closer to the line or network side equipment. The Timeplex Link/2+ also has the ability to perform trunking with the Promina multiplexer.

The Timeplex Link/2+ has both manual rerouting (via patch panels) and automatic rerouting capabilities. The Link/2+ is capable of numerous loopbacks—too many to list here.

Figure N-1 shows a local bidirectional loopback on the local Timeplex Link/2+. This type of loopback provides both a LOCAL to LOCAL loopback and a LOCAL to REMOTE loopback at the same time. It will loop traffic from your internal local LAN network back to itself through the local Timeplex Link/2+; and will loop traffic from the remote end back to the remote end through the local Timeplex Link/2+. This loopback allows you to verify that all the equipment on your local network is functioning properly through the local Timeplex Link/2+. This loopback also verifies that all equipment on the remote network and the Timeplex Link/2+ network is operating properly through your local Timeplex Link/2+.

Figure N-1 *Local Timeplex Link/2+ with local bidirectional loopback*

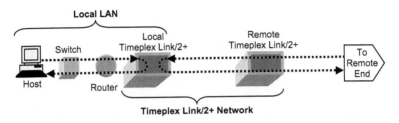

Figure N-2 shows a remote bidirectional loopback on the local Timeplex Link/2+. This type of loopback provides both a REMOTE to LOCAL loopback and a REMOTE to REMOTE loopback at the same time. It will loop traffic from your internal local LAN network through the Timeplex Link/2+ network and then back to itself through the remote Timeplex Link/2+; and will loop traffic from the remote end back to the remote end through the remote Timeplex Link/2+. This loopback allows you to verify that all the equipment on your local network and the Timeplex Link/2+ network is functioning properly through the remote Timeplex Link/2+. This loopback also verifies that all equipment on the remote network is operating properly through the remote Timeplex Link/2+.

Figure N-2 *Local Timeplex Link/2+ with remote bidirectional loopback*

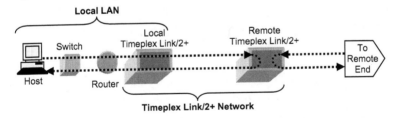

APPENDIX O

DTE and DCE

Brief Notes on DTE and DCE

Data Terminal Equipment (DTE) devices are more popularly known as the device on the user end receiving a service such as workstations, printers and router serial interfaces.

Data Communications Equipment or Data Circuit-Terminating Equipment (DCE) devices typically provide the clocking for DTE devices. Clocking, also known as timing, tells a device when to send the next bit and when to receive the next bit. DCE devices are known as the device, such as a modem or Channel Service Unit/Data Service Unit (CSU/DSU), on the network (Line) end providing a service and a path to the user end within the enterprise as shown in Figure O-1.

Figure O-1 *DTE and DCE control signals between Enterprise and ISP devices*

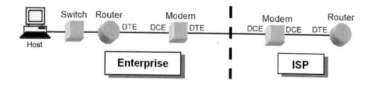

A device, such as a router, can have an interface that is either a DTE (which is normally the case) when facing the WAN or a service provider or have an interface that is a DCE—such as when two routers are connected back-to-back in a lab environment.

The terms DTE and DCE may not mean the same thing for every situation. It depends on which portion of the network we are talking about. The following are some differences in DTE and DCE devices based on their application on the network:

- Ethernet applications
- Serial (network/line side) applications
- Like-device applications

Ethernet applications

This application involves devices only within the same Enterprise.

- DTE devices are typically on the user end of the Enterprise such as workstations and printers.
- DCE devices are typically on the network (Line) end of the Enterprise such as modems and multiplexers.

Serial (network/line side) applications

This application involves the connection between the Enterprise and the Service Provider.

- DTE devices are typically on the Enterprise end such as modems and multiplexers, routers.
- DCE devices are typically on the Service Provider end such as ISP modems and multiplexers.

Like-device applications

In this application, the devices are the same—such as modem to modem or router to router—regardless if both devices are within the same Enterprise or lab environment, or if one device is in the Enterprise and the other is at the Service Provider.

- In like-device applications, such as modem to modem or router to router, one of the device's interfaces is typically chosen as the DTE and the other device's interface is selected as the DCE.
- In like-device applications, the device that is receiving services (such as an Enterprise modem) is typically the DTE, and the device

providing service (such as the Service Provider modem) is typically the DCE.

Note: These are not hard fast rules, and may differ at various locations. For modems, see the manufacture's user manual to configure the modem or other network devices for DTE or DCE.

DTE/DCE Control Signals

The following DTE/DCE control signals are given to show how these signals work between two devices. However, these signals can be "faked" through the use of null modem cables.

DTR = Data Terminal Ready
- DTE device is online and ready to receive data.
- Transmitted by the DTE's DTR line to the DCE's Date Set Ready (DSR) line, and does not wait for a signal or answer from the DCE's DSR line.
- Typically, this DTR signal is always on or set high.

DSR = Data Set Ready
- DCE device is ready to receive data.
- Transmitted by the DCE's DSR line to the DTE's Data Terminal Ready (DTR) line, and does not wait for a signal or answer from the DTE's DTR line.
- Typically, this DSR signal is always on or set high.

RTS = Request To Send
- DTE device is ready to send data to the DCE.
- Transmitted by the DTE's RTS line to the DCE's Clear to Send (CTS) line.
- The DTE device will not transmit data traffic until it receives an answer back from the DCE's CTS line.
- This RTS signal will go high (or on) only when it is ready to send data to the DCE device.

CTS = Clear To Send
- DCE device is ready for the DTE device to send data traffic.
- Transmitted by the DCE's CTS line to the DTE's Request to Send (RTS) line in response to the DTE's RTS signal.
- A high (or on) CTS signal from the DCE grants permission to the DTE to send data. If the DCE is busy processing other data, it will send a low (or off) CTS signal back to the DTE indicating it is not ready to receive data.

CD = Carrier Detect or Data Carrier Detect (DCD)
- Indicates a communication link between two modem devices or between a modem (DCE) and a DTE device (e.g. router or computer).
- Transmitted by the DCE or DTE at one end to represent a good communication link with the device at the other end that receives the CD signal.
- Connects to the CD line at both ends.

RD = Receive Data
- Data received by the DTE from the DCE.
- The RD signal is typically viewed with respect to the DTE, regardless of whether you're looking at the DTE or DCE device. In other words, on the DTE device, the RD represents data that is received by the DTE (from the DCE). On the DCE device, the RD represents data that is sent (by the DCE) to the DTE.
- Connects the Receive Data (RD) line on one end to the Transmit Data (TD) line on the other end.

TD = Transmit Data
- Data sent by the DTE to the DCE.
- The TD signal is typically viewed with respect to the DTE, regardless of whether you're looking at the DTE or DCE device. In other words, on the DTE device, the TD represents data that is sent from the DTE (to the DCE). On the DCE device, the TD represents data that is received (by the DCE) from the DTE.

- Connects the Transmit Data (TD) line on one end to the Receive Data (RD) line on the other end.

RC = Receive Clock
- DTE device is receiving timing signal from the DCE device.
- Connects the Receive Clock (RC) line to the Transmit Clock (TC) line.

TC = Transmit Clock
- DCE device is transmitting timing signal to the DTE device.
- Typically, the DCE device provides the transmit clock.
- Connects the Transmit Clock (TC) line to the Receive Clock (RC) line.

APPENDIX P

Modems

The word modem is actually a combination of two words: "*mod*" in modulator and "*dem*" in demodulator. Traditional modems are used to convert digital signals to analog signals (modulate) for transmission on telephone lines, and to convert analog signals back to digital signals (demodulate). Today, the word modem is oftentimes used interchangeably with the word CSU/DSU; however, technically there is one basic difference between the two.

A modem that receives a digital signal from another device, such as a router, and converts (modulates) it into an analog signal for transmission across telephone lines is technically called a modem.

A modem that receives a digital signal from another device, such as a router, and transmits it across digital serial leased lines (instead of analog phone lines), such as T1 circuit, is popularly known as a Channel Service Unit/Data Service Unit (CSU/DSU).

The CSU portion talks with the service provider (SP) which is typically the Data Communications Equipment or Data Circuit-Terminating Equipment (DCE) end. The DSU portion talks with the local user or Data Terminal Equipment (DTE) end.

Most of these CSU/DSU modems are standalone devices but can also be incorporated into other devices such as a router serial interface with an integrated CSU/DSU.

There are also fiber modems and Synchronous Optical Networking (SONET) multiplexers (MUX's) that convert digital signals to optical signals, and vice versa.

In satellite communications (SATCOM) and line-of-sight (LOS) communications, there are also different types of modems, also known as modulators, at various stages of frequency translation. In SATCOM, there are channel modulators, group modulators, and super-group modulators producing the "baseband", also known as the line frequency. Each successively higher level modulator produces a higher level frequency translation output—the baseband being the highest among these types of modems. Figure P-1 shows a variety of modem and multiplexer equipment that can be used for SATCOM communications.

Figure P-1 *Possible satellite equipment configurations on local end SATCOM*

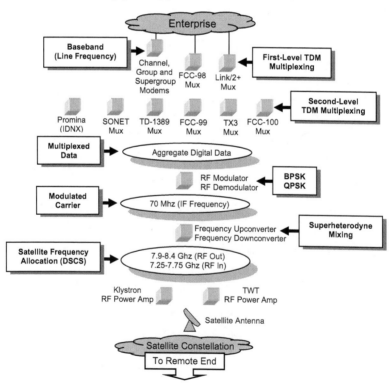

As shown in Figure P-1, there are also RF modems (modulators) that convert TDM digital data to an aggregate RF frequency, such as a 70 MHz Intermediate Frequency (IF) signal. This 70 MHz IF signal would then be fed to a frequency upconverter that would convert the 70 MHz IF to the final satellite frequency range, such as 7.9–8.4 GHz for the Defense Satellite Communications System (DSCS), for transmission from the satellite antenna.

APPENDIX Q

Troubleshooting with Modem Loopbacks

During troubleshooting, you may become involved in performing modem loopbacks. Unfortunately, modem loopbacks differ in names and direction of loopbacks based on the manufacturer. Never assume the name or direction of a loopback for one type of modem applies to another type of modem. If uncertain, check the manufacturer's user manual on that particular modem—it could save you a lot of time and error in troubleshooting.

Types of Modem Loopbacks

When performing loopbacks, it's important to distinguish the direction of loopbacks based on two different viewpoints:
- Loopbacks viewed by your local end
- Loopbacks viewed by your remote end

Three loopbacks are possible at each end (which is different depending on if the modem loop is accomplished by the local end or remote end). Either end can be the remote end or local end depending on which end is accomplishing the loopback on the modem—it's all a matter of point of reference as seen by each end. These principles about the direction of modem loopbacks can be applied to other networking devices, such as multiplexers or Promina/IDNX, but keep in mind these other networking devices may call their loop directions by different names too. When troubleshooting using loopbacks on networking devices, you should always clarify with the distant end (that you are troubleshooting with) the direction of the loop.

Loopbacks Viewed from Your Local End

Remote to local loopback
- The loop is placed on the remote modem toward your local modem.
- Your local end can see the modem loop from another device (e.g. router, switch) within your local network.
- The remote end cannot see the loop from another device (e.g. router, switch) within their network.
- The remote end should see the looped circuit as "down" from another device (e.g. router, switch) within their network.

Local to remote loopback
- The loop is placed on your local modem toward the remote end.
- The remote end can see the loop from another device (e.g. router, switch) within their network.
- Your local end cannot see the loop from another device (e.g. router, switch) within your local network.
- Your local end should see the looped circuit as "down" from another device (e.g. router, switch) within your local network.

Local to local loopback
- The loop is placed on your local modem toward your local network.
- Your local end can see the modem loop from another device (e.g. router, switch) within your local network.
- The remote end cannot see the loop from another device (e.g. router, switch) within their network.
- The remote end should see the looped circuit as "down" from another device (e.g. router, switch) within their network.

Loopbacks Viewed from Your Remote End

Remote to local loopback
- The loop is placed on your local modem toward the remote end.
- The remote end can see the loop from another device (e.g. router, switch) within their network.

- Your local end cannot see the loop from another device (e.g. router, switch) within your local network.
- Your local end should see the looped circuit as "down" from another device (e.g. router, switch) within your local network.

Local to remote loopback
- The loop is placed on the remote modem toward your local modem.
- Your local end can see the modem loop from another device (e.g. router, switch) within your local network.
- The remote end cannot see the loop from another device (e.g. router, switch) within their network.
- The remote end should see the looped circuit as "down" from another device (e.g. router, switch) within their network.

Local to local loopback
- The loop is placed on the remote modem toward the remote end.
- The remote end can see the loop from another device (e.g. router, switch) within their network.
- Your local end cannot see the loop from another device (e.g. router, switch) within your local network.
- Your local end should see the looped circuit as "down" from another device (e.g. router, switch) within your local network.

Loopbacks on Particular Modem Models

Different modem models use different names to describe the exact location of the loop within the modem device and the direction of the loop. Always review the manufacturer user's manual on the specific modem you are performing loops on.

APPENDIX R

Troubleshooting with PairGain Campus T1 Modem

The PairGain Campus T1 modem is a full-duplex DSL modem manufactured by ADC Telecommunications that has a maximum data rate of 1.544 Mbps (T1). You can perform loopbacks on the PairGain modem to help you troubleshoot problems across the network. Following are some loopbacks used by the PairGain modem.

Local interface loopback

If you want a "LOCAL to LOCAL loop" on your local PairGain modem (a loop on your local end PairGain modem facing toward your local enterprise equipment), you would emplace a "local interface loopback" as shown in Figure R-1.

This type of local loopback will loop traffic from your internal local LAN network back to itself through the Data port of your local PairGain modem; and will block and bring down traffic from the remote end. This allows you to verify that all the equipment on your local network up to the Data port of the local PairGain modem is functioning properly.

Figure R-1 *PairGain Campus T1 modem local interface loopback (local-to-local loopback)*

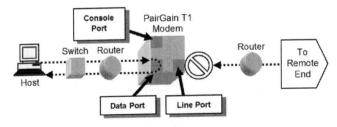

Here are some important notes about the local interface loopback on the PairGain modem:

- The loop is created at the local modem "Data port".
- Signals received from local equipment are sent to the local modem Data port where it loops back to the local equipment.
- This loop removes the local and remote PairGain Campus T1 modems circuitry from the loop; and tests only the local equipment and cable connected to the local PairGain Campus T1 modem at the end where this loop is created.
- The local end can see the modem loop from another device (e.g. router or switch) within their local network.
- The remote end cannot see the loop from another device (e.g. router or switch) within their network; and should see the looped circuit as "down".

Local HDSL loopback

The local HDSL loopback is another "LOCAL to LOCAL loop" on your local PairGain modem (a loop on your local end PairGain modem facing toward your local enterprise equipment), as shown in Figure R-2.

This type of local loopback will loop traffic from your internal local LAN network back to itself through the Line port of your local PairGain modem; and will block and bring down traffic from the remote end. This allows you to verify that all the equipment on your local network up to the Line port of the local PairGain modem is functioning properly.

Figure R-2 *PairGain Campus T1 modem local HDSL loopback (local-to-local loopback)*

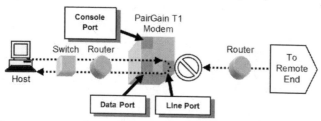

Here are some important notes about the local HDSL loopback on the PairGain modem:

- The loop is created at the local modem "Line port".

- Signals received from local equipment are sent through the local modem Data port to the Line port where it loops back to the local equipment.

- This loop includes the local PairGain Campus T1 modem circuitry in the loop, and also tests the local equipment and cable connected to the local PairGain Campus T1 at the end where this loop is placed.

- The local end can see the modem loop from another device (e.g. router, switch) within their local network.

- The remote end cannot see the loop from another device (e.g. router, switch) within their network.

- The remote end should see the looped circuit as "down" from another device (e.g. router, switch) within their network.

Remote interface loopback

If you want a "REMOTE to LOCAL loop" (a loop on the directly connected distant end's PairGain modem facing your local site) or a "REMOTE to REMOTE" loop (a loop the remote end can use), you would emplace a "remote interface loopback" on the distant end's PairGain modem as shown in Figure R-3.

Figure R-3 *PairGain Campus T1 modem remote interface loopback (remote-to-local loopback)*

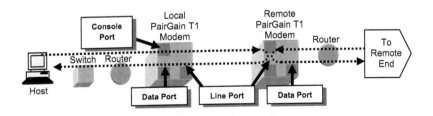

This type of loopback provides a bidirectional loop at the remote PairGain modem. It will loop traffic from your local network back to itself across the WAN through the Line port at the remote PairGain modem;

and will loop traffic from the remote end back to itself through Line port at the remote PairGain modem. This allows you to verify that all the equipment across the WAN and your local network is functioning properly through the remote PairGain modem; and allows the distant end to verify that their equipment is functioning properly through the remote PairGain modem.

Here are some important notes about the remote interface loopback on the PairGain modem:

- This loop command is initiated at the local modem to create a loop at the remote modem's "Data port".
- This loop command also produces a bi-directional loop at the remote modem's Data port.

Note: With a bi-directional loop, both ends can see the loop from another device (e.g. router, switch), and both ends can check their local end connections to the modem in a bi-directional loop.

- Signals received from the local end equipment are sent through the local PairGain Campus T1 modem (that initiated this loop command), across the communication link (HDSL) line, to the remote PairGain Campus T1 Data port where it loops back to the local end modem that initiated this loop command.
- Signals from the remote end equipment are sent through the remote PairGain Campus T1 modem where it loops back to the remote ends equipment.
- This loop includes the entire system, testing both the local and remote PairGain Campus T1 modems and the path between the two modems.

APPENDIX S

Troubleshooting with ASM-40 RAD Modem

The ASM-40 modem is a full-duplex synchronous short range CSU/DSU modem manufactured by RAD that has a maximum data rate of 2.048 Mbps (E1) in 13 selectable data rates with a maximum range of 1.75 km (1.1 miles). You can perform loopbacks on the ASM-40 modem to help you troubleshoot problems across the network. Following are some loopbacks used by the ASM-40 modem.

Analog (ANA) loopback

If you want a "LOCAL to LOCAL loop" on your local ASM-40 modem (a loop on your local end asm-40 modem facing toward your local enterprise equipment), you would emplace an "analog (ANA) loopback" as shown in Figure S-1.

This type of local loopback will loop traffic from your internal local LAN network back to itself through the your local ASM-40 modem; and will block and bring down traffic from the remote end. This allows you to verify that all the equipment on your local network up to the local ASM-40 modem is functioning properly.

Figure S-1 *ASM-40 modem analog (ANA) loopback (local-to-local loopback)*

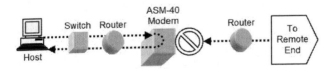

Here are some important notes about the analog (ANA) loopback on the ASM-40 modem:

- The loop is created at the local ASM-40 RAD modem toward local equipment.
- Signals received from local equipment are sent to the local ASM-40 modem where it loops back to the local equipment.
- This loop tests the local ASM-40 modem circuitry and the local equipment and cable connected to the local ASM-40 modem.
- Your local end can see the modem loop from another device (e.g. router, switch) within your local network.
- The remote end cannot see the loop from another device (e.g. router, switch) within their network.
- The remote end should see the looped circuit as "down" from another device (e.g. router, switch) within their network.

Remote (REM) loopback

The Remote (REM) loopback is a "REMOTE to LOCAL loop" on the distant end ASM-40 modem (a loop on the remote end ASM-40 modem facing toward your local network) as shown in Figure S-2.

Figure S-2 *ASM-40 remote (REM) loopback (remote-to-local loopback)*

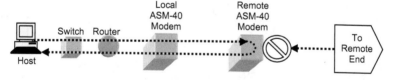

This type of loopback will loop traffic from your internal local LAN network back to itself through the remote ASM-40 modem; and will block and bring down traffic from the remote end. This allows you to verify that all the equipment on your local network across the WAN up to the remote ASM-40 modem is functioning properly.

Here are some important notes about the remote (REM) loopback on the ASM-40 modem:

- This loop command is initiated at the local modem to create a loop at the remote ASM-40 RAD modem.

- Signals received from local equipment are sent through the local modem (that initiated this loop command), across the communication link (HDSL) line, to the remote ASM-40 modem where it loops back to the local end modem that initiated this loop command.

- This loop includes the entire system, testing both the local and remote ASM-40 RAD modems and the path between the two modems.

- From your local modem's viewpoint, this loop also includes your local equipment and cabling connected to your local ASM-40 RAD modem.

- Your local end can see the modem loop from another device (e.g. router or switch) within your local network.

- This loop command does not produce a bi-directional loop.

- The remote end cannot see the loop from another device (e.g. router or switch) within their network; and should see the looped circuit as "down" from another device (e.g. router or switch) within their network.

Digital (DIG) loopback

If you want a "LOCAL to REMOTE loop" (a loop on your local ASM-40 PairGain modem facing the remote site), you would place a "digital (DIG) loopback" on your local end ASM-40 modem as shown in Figure S-3.

This type of loopback will loop traffic from remote end back to itself through the local ASM-40 modem; and will block and bring down traffic from your local LAN network. This allows the distant end to verify that all the equipment on their network across the WAN up to your local ASM-40 modem is functioning properly.

Figure S-3 *ASM-40 digital (DIG) loopback (locate-to-remote loopback)*

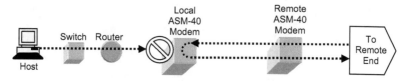

Here are some important notes about the digital (DIG) loopback on the ASM-40 modem:

- The loop is created at the local ASM-40 RAD modem toward the distant end remote equipment.
- Signals from the distant end remote equipment are sent through the remote ASM-40 RAD modem, across the HDSL line, to the local ASM-40 RAD modem (that initiated this loop command) where it loops back to the distant end's remote equipment.
- This loop includes the entire system, testing both the local and remote ASM-40 modems and the path between the two modems.
- This loop also allows the distant end to test their distant end equipment and cabling to their ASM-40 RAD modem.
- The remote end can see the loop (created at the local end modem) from another device (e.g. router or switch) within their network.
- This loop command does not produce a bi-directional loop.
- The local end (where this loop is created) cannot see the loop from another device (e.g. router or switch) within the local network; and should see the looped circuit as "down" from another device (e.g. router or switch) within the local network.

Appendix S: Troubleshooting with ASM-40 RAD Modem

APPENDIX T

Well-Known Port Numbers

Well-known port numbers are application ports below port number 1024 (ports 1 through 1023) and are typically used by servers, routers, and switches. Dynamic port numbers are ports 1024 and above, and are typically used by various types of application services. Below are some of the more common well-known port numbers.

PORT #	APPLICATION	KEYWORD	PROTOCOL TYPE
20	FTP (data)	ftp-data	TCP
21	FTP (control)	ftp	TCP
22	SSH	ssh	TCP
23	TELNET	telnet	TCP
25	SMTP	smtp	TCP
49	TACACS	tacacs	TCP & UDP
50	ESP	esp	UDP
51	AH	ah	TCP & UDP
53	DNS	domain	TCP & UDP
67	DHCP (server)	nameserver	UDP
68	DHCP (client)	nameserver	UDP
69	TFTP	tftp	UDP
80	HTTP	www or http	TCP
89	OSPF	ospf	n/a
110	POPMAIL v.3	pop3	TCP
123	NTP	ntp	UDP
143	IMAP4	imap4	TCP
161	SNMP	snmp	UDP
162	SNMP Trap	snmptrap	UDP
179	BGP	bgp	TCP
389	LDAP	ldap	TCP
443	HTTPS (with SSL or TLS)	https	TCP
500	IPsec	ipsec	UDP
520	RIP	rip	UDP
636	LDAPS (with SSL)	ldaps	TCP
639	MSDP	msdp	TCP
646	LDP	ldp	TCP & UDP

APPENDIX U

IPv4 Addressing Information

IPv4 Numbering Per Octet

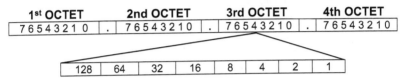

IPv4 Bitmask Number to Subnet Mask Conversion Table

128	192	224	240	248	252	254	255
/1	/2	/3	/4	/5	/6	/7	/8
/9	/10	/11	/12	/13	/14	/15	/16
/17	/18	/19	/20	/21	/22	/23	/24
/25	/26	/27	/28	/29	/30	/31	/32

Public (Registered/Routable) IPv4 Addresses

CLASS	RANGE OF FIRST OCTET	CAST TYPE
A	1.0.0.0 - 126.255.255.255	Unicast
B	128.0.0.0 – 191.255.255.255	Unicast
C	192.0.0.0 – 223.255.255.255	Unicast
D	224.0.0.0 – 239.255.255.255	Multicast
E	240.0.0.0 – 255.255.255.255	Reserved/ Experimental

Private (Unregistered/Non-routable) IPv4 Addresses
RFC 1918

CLASS	RANGE	CAST TYPE	Total Addresses
A	10.0.0.0 – 10.255.255.255	Unicast	16,777,216
B	172.16.0.0 – 172.31.255.255	Unicast	1,048,576
C	192.168.0.0 – 192.168.255.255	Unicast	65,536

APPENDIX V

IPv4 Multicast and Broadcast Address Allocation

PURPOSE	IPv4 ADDRESS
Reserved Link Local address (LAN segment only)	224.0.0.0 – 224.0.0.255
All systems on this subnet (Advertisements)	224.0.0.1
All routers on this subnet (Advertisements)	224.0.0.2
OSPF non-Designated Routers (Advertisements / Hello packets)	224.0.0.5
OSPF Designated Routers (Advertisements / Hello packets)	224.0.0.6
RIPv2 (Multicast advertisements)	224.0.0.9
EIGRP routers (Hello packets)	224.0.0.10
DHCP server/relay agent (Advertisements)	224.0.0.12
Range of all IP multicast-groups	224.0.0.0 – 239.255.255.255
Globally Scoped address (Internet)	224.0.1.0 – 238.255.255.255
Network Time Protocol (NTP)	224.0.1.1
Auto-RP groups (multicast)	224.0.1.39 and 224.0.1.40
Limited Scope address (LAN only)	239.0.0.0 – 239.255.255.255
RIPv1 (Broadcast advertisements)	255.255.255.255

APPENDIX W

Decimal to Binary to Hexadecimal Conversion

DECIMAL	BINARY	HEXADECIMAL
0	0000	0
1	0001	1
2	0010	2
3	0011	3
4	0100	4
5	0101	5
6	0110	6
7	0111	7
8	1000	8
9	1001	9
10	1010	A
11	1010	B
12	1100	C
13	1101	D
14	1110	E
15	1111	F
16	00010000	10
17	00010001	11
18	00010010	12
19	00010011	13
20	00010100	14
21	00010101	15
22	00010110	16
23	00010111	17
24	00011000	18
25	00011001	19
26	00011010	1A
27	00011011	1B
28	00011100	1C
29	00011101	1D
30	00011110	1E
31	00011111	1F
32	00100000	20
33	00100001	21
34	00100010	22
35	00100011	23
36	00100100	24
37	00100101	25
38	00100110	26
39	00100111	27
40	00101000	28
41	00101001	29
42	00101010	2A
43	00101011	2B
44	00101100	2C
45	00101101	2D
46	00101110	2E
47	00101111	2F

APPENDIX X

Cisco Administrative Distances

AD	ROUTING PROTOCOL
0	Directly connected interface (point-to-point)
0	Static route directed to a connected interface
1	Static route directed to an IP address
5	EIGRP (summary route)
20	eBGP (external)
90	EIGRP (internal)
100	IGP or IGRP
110	OSPF
115	IS-IS
120	RIP
140	EGP
170	EIGRP (external)
200	iBGP (internal)
255	Unknown/Unreachable

APPENDIX Y

Juniper Preference Values (Administrative Distances)

Preference	ROUTING PROTOCOL
0	Directly connected interface (point-to-point)
1	NAT Proxy-ARP routes
4	System route
5	Static and static LSPs
7	RSVP-signaled LSPs
9	LDP-signaled LSPs
10	OSPF internal route
15	IS-IS Level 1 internal route
18	IS-IS Level 2 internal route
30	Redirects
40	Kernel
50	SNMP
55	Router discovery
100	RIP
100	RIPng (RIP for IPv6)
105	PIM
110	DVMRP
130	Aggregate
150	OSPF AS external routes
160	IS-IS Level 1 external route
165	IS-IS Level 2 external route
170	BGP
175	MSDP

APPENDIX Z

Alcatel-Lucent Preference Values
(Administrative Distances)

Preference	ROUTING PROTOCOL
0	Directly connected interface (point-to-point)
1	Static
10	OSPF non-external route
100	RIP
130	Generated or aggregate
150	OSPF AS external routes
170	BGP

Also By Frank McClain

Book of the Year award winner *The Ultimate Job Hunting Guidebook*, award-winning *YOU'RE HIRED!* and *The Ultimate Job Hunting Guidebook for Military Veterans*

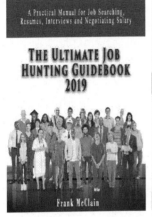  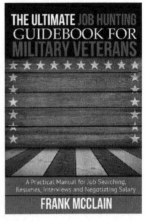

IT Questions & Answers For IT Job Interviews, Volume 2
IT Questions & Answers For IT Job Interviews, Volume 3
IT Questions & Answers For IT Job Interviews, Volume 4
IT Questions & Answers For IT Job Interviews, Volume 5
IT Questions & Answers For IT Job Interviews, Volume 6

Did you like *IT Questions & Answers For IT Job Interviews, Volume 1?* **Did this book help you?** Then please do me this huge favor and write a book review on the Amazon website where you purchased this book. At the bottom of the webpage, click the "**Write a customer review**" button. It's that simple. As an indie author seeking customer reviews for my book, I greatly appreciate and value your review—*Thank you*!

Give this book as a gift to a friend or family member.

If this book helped you, tell your connected friends about this book on social media. It's a great way to let your friends know about a good read that will help both you and them in your careers—and your friends will thank you for it! Let me be one of the first to say *THANK YOU* for introducing your friends to a book that will no doubt enhance their careers.

One Last Thing . . .

Be the first to find out when the next books I'm writing will come out by signing up on my email list at this link: http://bit.ly/2ffZcmx. I will not sell your email to marketers nor contact you for any other reason than to let you know when my next books are out on the market. When you sign up, you'll receive a confirmation email from "**Frank McClain confirmations@madmimi.com**"; so check your spam inbox if you don't see this confirmation email in your email Inbox. It's that simple.

Frank McClain